TRADE GOODS

TRADE GOODS

A STUDY OF INDIAN CHINTZ

in the Collection of the

Cooper-Hewitt Museum of Decorative Arts and Design

Smithsonian Institution

ALICE BALDWIN BEER

SMITHSONIAN INSTITUTION PRESS · WASHINGTON, D.C. · 1970

Contents

Foreword

It is a pleasure to record at this time the writer's gratitude and indebtedness to scholars, historians, and collectors whose work has preceded and made possible the present study: first, to the late George P. Baker, whose great two-volume work, *Calico Painting and Printing in the East Indies, in the Seventeenth and Eighteenth Centuries*, introduced the writer to the technique of painting cottons; next to the articles of the late Paul R. Schwartz, whose translation of the Beaulieu Manuscript and analysis of that document, appearing in the *Journal of Indian Textile History*, 1956, added important information on the methods of Indian cotton painting and dyeing. Lastly, the writer is indebted to the studies of John Irwin and Mrs. Katharine B. Brett, contributed to the *Journal of Indian Textile History* from its first number in 1955, to their many articles appearing elsewhere, and finally to their collaboration on the great work, *The Origins of Chintz*, published in 1970, which presented this student with richly enlarged sources of information. To the last-named authors and to the late Paul R. Schwartz, the writer is deeply thankful—not only for their written words, but for much kindly assistance so patiently given over many years.

The aid, in a dozen different ways, helpful criticism, and forbearance of colleagues in the Museum is herewith acknowledged. But special thanks are here offered to Milton Sonday, Assistant Curator, and Sandra Shaffer, Technical Assistant, in the Department of Textiles, for the generous contribution of their time and skills, in ways too numerous to catalogue.

The writer is indebted to a bequest for research from the Estate of the late Irene Lewisohn, which made possible study abroad for two months and the professional services of two able research assistants, Miss Babette Hanish, and Mrs. Julie Merwin.

This study was undertaken to accompany the great exhibition of Indian Chintz from the collections of the Victoria and Albert Museum in London and the Royal Ontario Museum in Toronto, held in the Cooper-Hewitt Museum, 26 June to 6 August 1970. For the costs of preparing and mounting such a large exhibition of rare material, the Museum acknowledges with gratitude a grant from the John D. Rockefeller III Fund.

ALICE BALDWIN BEER

Definition of Chintz

Cit, chit, cheetes, schite, chites, chint, chints: Thus the spelling of a word, constantly used in records of the factors of the East India Company, or of the various travelers who made their way to India in the seventeenth century. As:

1630, Peter Mundy, "In this place (Sironj) are made great quantities of excellent pintadoes or chints, much nominated and esteemed throughout India."

1652, Tavernier, " . . . embarking on a vessel . . . laden with muslins and chites or coloured calicoes, the flowered decorations of which is all done by hand, which makes them more beautiful and more expensive than when printed."

1665, Bernier, "The superior colours of the Maslipatam chittes or cloths, painted by hand (peintes au pinceau) . . . are also ascribed to the water peculiar to that town."

1669–1679, Bowery, "Metchlipatam Affordeth many very good and fine Commodities . . . divers sorts of Chint curiously flowered, which doth much represent flowered Sattin, of Curious, Lively Colours . . . "

Chintz: A printed or spotted cotton cloth, Portuguese Chita. . Makr. . Chit, Hindi, chint. The word in this last form occurs (c. 1590) in the *Ain-i-Akbari*. It comes apparently from the Sanskrit Chitroc, "variegated, speckled" . . . (From Yule, Henry and A.C. Burnell, *Hobson-Jobson, A Glossary of Anglo-Indian Words and Phrases.*) Chitta: "spotted cloth," (cf. chitt, chat) Kamaoni, chit 'calico', Nepali, chit, Assamese, sit, Bengali, chit, Oriya, chita, Hindi, chit, chīt, Kashmiri, chith . . . Sindhi, chita, Punjabi, chit, *Gujarati, chit f. 'chintz'*. (From Ralph L. Turner, *A Comparative Dictionary of the Indo-Aryan Languages*, Fascicule IV, pp. 271, 272, 276.)

It is highly probable that to most of our readers the word *chintz* conveys an image of some flowered material, cotton, highly glazed, and sold for curtains or upholstery fabric. Indeed, today plain glazed cotton in various colors is also sold under the name of chintz. In seventeenth-century India the word referred to a specially designed painted or printed cotton, sometimes glazed, which was used for clothing and traded in the Spice Islands, or Persia and the Near East. This was a trade, ages old, conducted largely by Arab seamen, who, before the Portuguese, carried the cottons of India, flowered, plain, striped, or woven with gold, to remote islands "eastward" where they were bartered for pepper, spices, gold, and other goods, salable in India; or to Persia, or up the Red Sea to Egypt, or Africa, in exchange there for ivory, or gold, or horses for the warriors of India.

When, in the middle of the seventeenth century, the Dutch and English, now busily trading in India, realized that there might be a market for the Indian "chints" they began to suggest, rather to dictate, styles of design; patterns were sent out and by the end of the seventeenth century the popularity of the Indian chintz was established in Europe and England. The story of the development of block printing in Holland, England, and France as a result of these importations is too familiar to bear repetition.

Since this study is written in English and for an English-speaking audience, and since the larger part of the sources consulted are in English, the story of these Trade Goods has developed from the founding of the English East India Company in 1600; and, although an attempt has been made by brief references to remind the reader of the importance of the Dutch and later the French in India, the point of view is that of the English Adventurer.

HISTORY

The Merchant Adventurers

Shylock: Three thousand ducats for three months and Antonio to be bound.

Bassanio: Your answer to that.

Shylock: Antonio is a good man.

Bassanio: Have you heard any imputation to the contrary?

Shylock: Ho, no, no, no, no: my meaning in saying he is a good man is to have you understand me that he is sufficient. Yet his means are in supposition: He hath an argosy bound to Tripolis, another to the Indies; I understand moreover upon the Rialto, he hath a third to Mexico, a fourth for England, and other ventures he hath squandered abroad. But ships are but boards, sailors but men; there be land-thieves and water-thieves—I mean pirates—and then there is the peril of waters, winds and rocks. The man is notwithstanding sufficient. Three thousand ducats: I think I may take his bond.[1]

Though he set the scene of his play in Venice, for so long the great entrepôt for trade with the East, he has given us a picture of English trade in far lands, its dangers, risks, and perils, as of the year 1595 or 1596, the probable date of Shakespeare's *Merchant of Venice*; he might have been speaking for the Merchant Adventurers of London who were at that moment considerably troubled by the fact that the Dutch had already sent out two expeditions by the Cape of Good Hope to the Indies and felt that something more organized was called for than the capturing of Spanish and Portuguese prizes, or the slow but profitable operations through the "Turkey Company," afterward the Levant Company. The way lay open, had been known since 1498 when Vasco da Gama made his famous voyage to India around the Cape of Good Hope and began, at Calicut, the establishment of the great Portugese Empire in the East. And Magellan's little fleet had circumnavigated the globe. Though he died in the effort to find the Spice Islands, killed in the Philippines, one of his ships limped home; the voyage took from 1519 to 1522. Drake had defied the Spanish, and between 1577 and 1580 sailed west on his famous circumnavigation, found the Spice Islands, and returned with much booty in 1580. Then the Armada, defeated in 1588, with the aid of certain Dutch forces and a fortunate wind, to say nothing of superior English seamanship, put an end to the danger of invasion by Philip of Spain.

But England had been a latecomer in this era of enlarged comprehension of the world's extent. That little huddle of islands at the north of the map was far removed from what had for centuries been the world's center of activity—the Mediterranean. Around that inner sea the Italians, Spanish, and Portuguese had voyaged and set forth to explore. And to this sea had come, for many centuries, through various powers and principalities of the Near East, by caravan, by Arabian traders from the Indian Ocean and the Red Sea, the treasures of some remote land, its place and extent unknown, the jewels, gold, slaves, materials, but above all the essential spices, myrrh, frankincense, cinnamon, cloves, nutmeg, and pepper. How the source of the spices and the routes of their delivery were so long "the best kept trade secret of all time"[2] is too long a story here to tell. The ports of delivery varied according to governments in power; in the period following the Fourth Crusade, 1204, came the rise of Pisa, Genoa, and Venice as great trading centers, and the Eastern treasure, particularly spices, delivered to Alexandria was there loaded onto the Venetian fleet and carried by slow stages across to Venice.

To understand the antiquity of the commerce, one may read that anonymous record of trade, the rhythmic title of which demands repetition, *The Periplus of the Erythraean Sea*.[3] It is the description, the log book, of some Greek trader, a Roman subject in Egypt, sailing along the east coast of Africa, the Red Sea, and the Indian Ocean to a port on the west coast of India called Barygaza. To this and to other ports of this coast the author carefully lists goods traded, carried thither, and those exported.

> They send large ships to the market towns on account of the great quantity and bulk of pepper and malabathrum. There are imported here in the first place, a great quantity of coin: topaz, thin clothing, not much, figured linens, antimony, coral, crude glass, copper, tin, lead; wine, not much, but as much as at Barygaza; realgar and orpiment; and wheat enough for the sailors, for this is not dealt in by the merchants there. There is exported pepper, which is produced in quantity in only one region near these markets, a district called Cottonara. Beside this there are exported great quantities of fine pearls, ivory, silk cloth; spikenard from the Ganges, malabathrum from places in the interior, transparent stones of all kinds, diamonds and saphires, and tortoise-shell; that from Chryse Island, and that taken among the islands along the coast of Damirica. They make the voyage to this place who set out from Egypt about the month of July, that is Epiphi.

While the jewels, ivory, and incense might kindle ambition, the key word here is PEPPER.

The Periplus dates about 60 A.D., according to its most excellent editor, Wilfred H. Schoff. Now it is not here suggested that a review of exploration from classical antiquity is in order; nor shall we quote at length from Marco Polo, the journal of whose journeys has much to do with the awakening of Europeans to the existence of lands and opportunities in the remote East. But it was the determination to find the source of pepper and other spices that drove the Italians, the Spaniards, and Portuguese to the series of explorations in the fifteenth and sixteenth century which landed Spain in possession of Central and South America and the Philippines, and brought Portugal in control of the Indian markets.

For years historians have referred to the "spice trade," the effort to find the "Spice Islands." Why? Without reviewing their importance in religion, ritual use, and medicine for centuries before the Christian era, let a few statements of value suffice. Here Mr. Frederic Rosengarten's *The Book of Spices* is illuminating. In 1180, in the reign of Henry II of England, a Pepperers' Guild of London was established; later it was incorporated into a Spicers' Guild, succeeded in 1429 by the present Grocers' Company. It was granted a charter by Henry VI to sell wholesale and to manage the trade in spices, drugs, and dye stuffs. The original spicers and pepperers were the forerunners of the apothecaries, who in turn became general medical practitioners.

> In the 13th century a pound of pepper cost the equivalent of 60 U.S. cents in Marseilles but over $1.00 in England. Peppercorns counted out one by one, were accepted as currency to pay taxes, tolls and rents, partly because of the shortage of gold and silver coins. Many European towns kept their accounts in pepper. Fortunate brides received pepper as a dowry.

By the late Middle Ages oriental spices were valued roughly as follows: A pound of saffron cost the same as a horse; a pound of ginger as much as a sheep; two pounds of mace would buy a cow. A German price table of 1393 lists a pound of nutmeg as worth seven fat oxen.

When one considers the wretched victuals of 15th century Europe it is easy to understand the extraordinary value placed on spices. Food was neither wholesome nor palatable. Spices were believed to have a beneficial preservative action in meat. . . . Spices . . . such as pepper, cinammon, ginger and cardamon, when mixed with the coarsest, dullest food, even the most repulsive fare, could make it more palatable. Spices were used to camouflage bad odors and it was believed their consumption would prevent illness.[4]

Later the same author concludes:

In an epoch when Europe knew nothing of sugar, tea, coffee, chocolate, potatoes, citrus fruits or tobacco, to say nothing of plumbing or refrigeration, Oriental spices supplied flavor and piquancy for food and drink and fragrant aromas to mask a multitude of unpleasant odors. . . . So useful, indeed indispensable, were spices that kings sent expeditions in search of them, merchants risked life and fortune to trade in them, wars were fought over them.

Although the merchants of London were not necessarily thus informed, the value of the spice trade was obvious to them, and had been increasingly so, and the spectacle of the Dutch taking root in the Indies, in spots strategic to the control of the spice trade, was too much. In 1599 the Association of Merchant Adventurers of London addressed a memorandum to the Lords of the Council for authority to apply to the Queen for her royal consent to a great new venture. They pointed out that "divers merchants, induced by the success of the viage performed by the Duche Naton, and being informed that the Duchemen prepare for a new viage, and to that ende have bought divers ships here, in Englande . . . have resolved to make a viage to the East Indies." Shrewdly they asked to be incorporated as a "jointe and united stock" and that they might be allowed to export foreign coin, a practice that later induced shudders among conservative economists.[5]

Protracted negotiations for peace with Spain delayed the plan. But at last the patent is granted, with those ringing words. "Elizabeth by the Grace of God, Queene of England, France and Ireland, Defendour of the Faith. . . . A priviledge for fifteene years granted by her Majestie to certain adventurers, for the discoverie of the trade for the East-Indies, the one and thirtieth of December, 1600."[6] An adventurer, by the way, was one who adventured his money in a voyage. The word has a swashbuckling sound to us today, but the merchants were underwriting a new venture in business.

It is probable that close at hand for consultation with the merchants had been Master Richard Hakluyt. Through his study of "cosmographie," his steady chronicling of the explorations, foreign and English, and the publications of his series of *Voyages*, he had contributed largely to the education of his fellow countrymen, and had become an authority consulted on several projects of exploration or settlement.[7] It was through his interest that the famous voyage of a young Dutchman, John Huyghen van Linschoten, had been translated into English and published in London in 1598. This amazing work, the record of Linschoten's ten years in India with the Portuguese, and the narrative of his return voyage—an experience

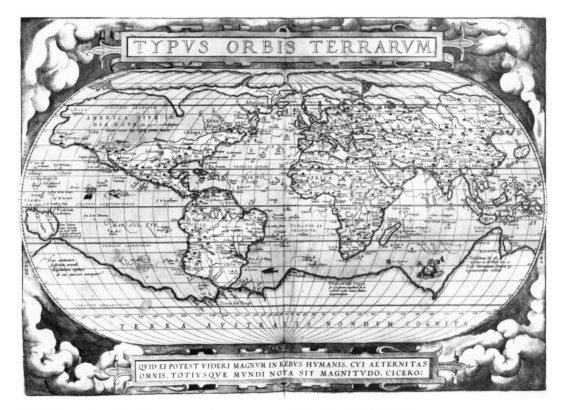

World map, Ortelius, *Theatre . . .* , Antwerp, 1571. New York Public Library.

calculated to chill an armchair voyager today—seems only to have excited ambitious readers of his time to venture fortune and life.

Hakluyt's third and last volume of his *Voyages*, a much expanded edition, appeared in September of 1600. In his determined pursuit of the record of exploration, foreign and English, and particularly his chronicle of the achievement of his countrymen, told in the rugged and beautiful language of his day, he stands as a main force in the instruction of his age. His legacy to us is a memorable chapter in history, one to which we turn for the background of England's adventure in the East.

If the impatient reader is wondering when the Indian cottons appear, it is *now*. While the Merchant Adventurers were keen on the trail of spices, they knew that success was largely a matter of trade. Goods must be found to barter for the pepper, cinnamon, cloves, and nutmeg, and enough information had reached them to show that various Indian cottons were the most acceptable goods in the Spice Islands.

To begin with, Ralph Fitch, who had gone overland to India with Newberry and had returned to London with his records, appears to have got as far as Siam. These records were published, making it known that

> In India there are few commodities which serve for Pegu, except Opium of Cambaia, painted cloth of S. Thomè or Masulipatam and white cloth of Bengala which is spent there in great quantity. They bring thither also much cotton yarne red coloured, with a root which they call Saia, which will never lose his color; it is very well sold here, and very much of it cometh yearly to Pegu. By your mony you lose much.

Further, he reports on ships from Malacca "laden with Sandall, Porcelanes, and other wares of China, and with Camphora of Borneo, and Pepper from Achen and Sumatra."[8]

Caesar Frederick, a Venetian who had been in India, 1563-1581, records much to the same effect:

> In the Indies there is not any marchandise that is good to bring to Pegu, unles it be at some time to bring Opium of Cambaia, and if he bring money he shall lose by it. . . . Now the commodities that come from S. Tomè are the only Marchandize for that place, which is the great quantity of cloth made there which they use in Pegu; which cloth is made of bombast woven and painted . . . which is of so great importance that a small bale of it will cost a thousand or two thousand duckets."[9]

In addition there was the already existing trade with the Barbary Coast and the Levant.

Especially the cotton cloth of India was important for barter in the Spice Islands for resale in North Africa and the Guinea Coast, seat of the slave trade, and for home consumption. And what to take out for trade in the Indies?

It has been said that what England sent to India was courage. To that should be added: men.[10]

To begin with, as a first test of courage, there was the voyage out. To us those wooden sailing ships may seem romantic. Their power was the wind in their sails and the skill of the navigator. They were dependent on the monsoons, and the routes were still incompletely charted. It is true they went armed, for there were the Portuguese to contend with, the pirates to ward off, and—though in 1600 they did not know it—there were the Dutch, as yet friendly competitors with whom they would ultimately fight. By today's standards these ships were dreadfully crowded and unsanitary. Certainly the dreaded scurvy and other ailments might incapacitate half a crew before they reached the Cape of "Buena Esperanza."

When on 21 September 1583 Linschoten reached India, he reported, "There dyed in our shippe 30 persons. Every man had been sicke once or twice and let bloode. This is commonly the number of men that ordinarily dyed in the ships, sometimes more, sometimes lesse."[11]

The first fleet of the East India Company sailed under the leadership of Sir James Lancaster. It consisted of five vessels, the largest of which, the *Red Dragon*, which carried Lancaster and John Davis, Pilot Major, was of 800 tons. The goods they took out were iron, tin, and wools. Be sure there were wools, for England needed a market for the oversupply of her staple and looked hopefully to the East to absorb her broadcloths and kerseys. Various articles were also carried as gifts to propitiate powerful, or unscrupulous persons: plate of considerable value, fans, plumes, looking glasses, armour, and swords.

When on the 9th of September, the fleet reached Table Bay at the Cape of Good Hope, scurvy was rampant among the sailors, and the crew of the *Dragon*, having had lemon juice issued by their experienced Commander, though infected were at least able to help the sick ashore. Here the fleet stayed, "refreshing themselves," as the current phrase ran, with fresh meat and water until the 20th of October. The unknown author of a "true and large discourse of the East India Voyage"[12] who was obviously a member of the crew of one vessel, reports that when they set sail there "were dead in the whole fleete at this time 107, and others that were sicke recovered to health." The same writer gives us at the end of his very detailed "discourse" the names of the men who died in each ship, amounting to the sad total of one hundred and eighty.

The rest of the voyage, with its sickness, death, and many mishaps, may be passed over. On the way up the east coast of Africa, Lancaster learned that a Dutch fleet was ahead of them. On the 5th of June, a year and four months after he had departed from England, Lancaster reached Achin, on the northwest tip of the Island of Sumatra, to find Dutch factors already settled there. Thus, at the start the Merchant Adventurers found the Dutch in the advantageous positions, in one of the prime sources of pepper. The Dutch welcomed the English however, and later, made an expedition with them toward the Straits of Malacca. Also the local ruler at Achin was cordial, received Lancaster with all honor, accepted the letter from King James, and gifts. Trading was carried on, and later Lancaster established a factory at Bantam on the Island of Java.

The activities of the Dutch in and about the islands, their determination to monopolize the spice trade, their superior number and support, however, eventually forced the English to concentrate their plans upon the mainland of India. Between 1601 and 1609 the English Company sent out five voyages totaling in all, fourteen ships; whereas between 1602 and 1607 the Dutch sent out five voyages totaling sixty-five ships. As we know, they had been trading in the Indian Archipelago since 1595, though the Netherlands East India Company was not formed until 1602. Steadily the Dutch drove the Portuguese from key positions, conquered islands, and where they conquered they built forts. The London Company continued to operate among the smaller islands, even reached Japan, though they did not hold this position as it did not pay. In those seas they learned, too, a commerce, ages old, of trading with the Chinese junks.

Finally, in 1618, the hot rivalry between the Dutch and the English came to a fight, off Patani, in the Gulf of Siam. The English were defeated, their leader, John Jourdain was killed, and the power of the Dutch established in the Archipelago.[13] This was not the end of Dutch competition with the English, for they established centers on the east coast of India, the Coromandel coast, at Pulicat and Masulipatam, and later, as we shall see, at other points on the Indian mainland; one particularly important center was Surat, on the west coast, as it became, early in the seventeenth century, the leading port for English trade.

The presence of the Dutch in India and the Indies is here emphasized because, as did the English, they became heavily involved in the production and trading of the painted cottons with which we are concerned.

Surat, for which the third English voyage aimed, was a most active port in the Province of Gujarat on the Gulf of Cambaya on the west coast of India, and was part of the dominions of the Mughal Emperor, Jahangir. This monarch, who styled himself "world conqueror," was indeed very powerful on land, and was surrounded by an enormous court which appears, from letters and descriptions of the time, to deserve that cliché, "glittering." His favorite son, Prince Khurram, the future Emperor Shahjahan, was Viceroy of Gujarat and so controlled Surat. The town lay a few miles from the mouth of the River Tapti, where a bar at the river's mouth stopped all but the lightest craft. The Portuguese also undertook to block the port to the English and harass their ships.

The little English fleet divided, William Keeling, the leader in the *Dragon* went on to Bantam while the *Hector*, commanded by William Hawkins, anchored off Surat. Here he planned to establish a factory, but all efforts were met with interference. Hawkins decided on a direct appeal to the Emperor, a letter to whom had been provided by King James. Though he was politely treated at first, he made the mistake of trying to give the impression that he was an ambassador; since he was a merchant he was disdained by Mughal authorities, and finally left for England. Hawkins was the first of a succession of factors who went with letters and gifts to the Emperor. But Portuguese influence was strong and not until Captain Thomas Best, arriving off Surat in 1612, defeated an attack by the Portuguese, was it possible to secure from the Gujarat officials the right to trade at Surat. Yet so uncertain was the state of relations, so constant the mistreatment of the factors, that the Company in London decided to appeal to the King to appoint an ambassador to the Emperor.

The Ambassador

Toward the end of this present yeere 1614, viz. in the beginning of January, His Majesty, at the request of the East India Company, sent Sir Thomas Roe, Knight, ambassadour to the Great Maghore, whome some corruptly call Mogall . . . unto whome this ambassadour had commission to make and contract a league between His Majesty and his subjects for comerce and traffique in his dominions, and to procure and establish a factory for our nation in sundry parts of his dominions, as well seaports as inland townes, with other instructions yet undiscovered. Hee is the first that ever was imployed in this his nature to any of those so farre remote easterne princes.[14]

Before his arrival at Surat hostilities had broken out between the Portuguese and Jahangir's government. At this point, in 1615 the English fleet under Nicholas Downton arrived in Swally Road, off Surat. The Portuguese were rash enough to provoke a battle, the Viceroy himself commanding a huge flotilla. In this action the Portuguese were defeated, and the reputation of the English considerably heightened. It was in this uneasy situation that Sir Thomas Roe arrived off Surat. He was armed with his commission, a letter from King James to the Emperor, and presents; he was armed also with a determination to secure for the Company trading rights, fair treatment, and a clear guarantee, or "firman" for the position of the English in the Mughal Empire.

He had need of all his diplomacy, his firmness of character, his ability to assert and maintain the position and privileges of his ambassadorial rank. From the first, he took a high and somewhat haughty attitude. It was as well. He landed in state, 6 September 1715, accompanied by the Commander of the fleet, the merchants, and a large armed guard of some eighty men. Here is his first encounter with representatives of the Governor of Surat.

At my landing, the cheefe officers of Suratt with about 30 companions wer sitting under an open tent upon good carpetts, in grave order. Coming almost to them and they not rising, I stayd and sent them woord I would not come further if they satte still; whereupon they all rose, and I entered the tent and went streight up and tooke my place in the midst of them. . . .[15]

The experience following this reception is an example of the abuse to which the factors had been subjected, for the Surat committee of welcome proposed first of all that the Ambassador and all his company be searched, for such, they said, was the regular proceeding of the port authorities. Sir Thomas, with considerable choler, refused, threatening to return to the ships. Yet, as they proceeded on horseback to the town, he found the Suratts, as he called them, dragging his companions from the saddle and attempting to search them. He rode back, laid his hand on his sword and called for a brace of pistols, and hanging them at his saddle declared these were his friends!

At Roe's description of the long struggle that followed we may laugh now, but we share his exasperation at the deceits and indignities imposed on him during his stay in Surat. His baggage, which had been sealed and was to have been delivered to his house, was held, and finally the Governor opened it and helped himself to what he chose. He was, of course, feeling for a bribe, and Roe was resolute to break this custom. Finally his firm stand, determination, and diplomacy won and he was enabled to make the long journey to Ajmere, where Jahangir was in residence at the time. Roe was well and courteously received by the Emperor.

So began a long four years of work, in which the Ambassador was at least partially successful in securing some of the guarantees he wished for the Company. His journal and letters draw for us a picture of the Mughal court and kingdom, and we learn through his experience how grasping, how childishly eager for bribes and gifts they were, from the Emperor to the lowest trader.

This matter of the importance of gifts plays a large part in the correspondence, not only of Roe, but of the factors who had preceded him and those who followed. Roe also makes, in his reports to the London Company, useful comments on what will and what will not sell.

He is advised by one of the Emperor's ministers that the English send too much cloth and "ill swords" and almost nothing else, and that everybody was weary of this. He urged instead that the rarities of China and Japan be secured, and from England, silk, gold, and silver and "good quality of arras for hangings" and the King would buy in quantity and every great man in proportion.[16] This suggestion of arras (tapestry) is made several times to the ambassador and factors.

Spices, Roe emphasizes, "sell to good profit, indigo and cotton cloth, are important"; he wishes "we had yearly 100 tons of pepper, 40 of cloves, 20 of mace and 20 of nutmegs." Also, China dishes and all sorts of fine ware, as "chestes, cabbenetts, bedsteades etc. to as good profit as in England. Taffaties imbrodered with gould silke in flowers, vearie well requested and rated. From these partes (the Far East) you maie be better furnished than from Europe." In a letter to the Company, 14 February 1618 was enclosed a long list: "Advise for Goods for Suratt." This is an interesting document on trade goods, too long to quote, which seems to sum up most of Roe's observation. He suggests limiting the amount of wool sent, stresses the importance of several kinds of jewelry, coral especially, and rare stones. Arras is again listed, "fresh and good colors. . . . Cloth of gould and silver branched, grograines or sattins that make a fine show mingled with fresh colors will raze money but to no great profit . . . " Then,

> Imbrodered coates of the Indian fashion, for our waistcoates they cannot use here. I have patternes of the King of divers sortes sent you. . . . And generally I give you this rule; whatsoever you send in this kind must be made by Indian patternes, for then they are of use and every bodies monie. Gloves, hangers (for swords?), scarfs: by these only they picke out the workes. Instead of sweet baggs, rownde cushions gathered like cloke bags, to leane upon. Any of this in needleworke or imbroiderie being fallen in value, for they have learned by ours to do as well. Boxes imbroidered will sell to profitt and great glasses. Some light coloured Norwich stuffs wrought in flowers for triall, the lighter the better . . .

Follows a long page of advice on presents, particularly to be given the Emperor. Sir Thomas is all in favor of fewer and finer, and he ends the paragraph with "Pictures of all sortes, if good, in constant request; some large storie; Diana this yere gave great content."[17]

In general his advice to the Company was that Surat was their best port, and that they will succeed so long as they can keep the Portuguese at bay. "Fear only keeps us in."

The Trade

Any exploration of the records of the East India Company, or of the notes of early travelers makes plain the great plenitude of textiles of Indian make, their essential character not only in India proper but in the Spice Islands and in Persia; while we are supposed to be strictly examining the painted cottons, we cannot overlook other materials and the importance of the trade. And as the Portuguese were on the ground before the English or Dutch their comments are in order.

Ludovico di Varthema was in the East from 1502 to 1508. Of Bengal, he wrote

Fifty ships are laden every year in this place with cotton and silk stuffs which stuffs are these [follow six Indian names]. These same stuffs go through all Turkey, through Syria, through Persia, through Arabia Felix, through Ethiopia and through all India. There are also here very great merchants in jewels, which come from other countries.[18]

As Varthema had come through Persia he had grounds for his statement.

Another Portuguese traveler in the East in about the year 1516, Duarte Barbosa filled two volumes with his reports. He was impressed with the "fair city of Cambaia" in west India. He tells us that in the city dwelt substantial merchants and men of great fortune and that there are

many craftsmen of mechanic work of many kinds, as in Flanders; and everything good cheap. Here are woven white cotton fabrics both fine and coarse, and others printed in patterns; also much silk cloth and coloured velvets of poor quality, velvety satins and taffeties, also thick carpets

And later, after some comments on the luxury of life in this city he tells us

They also make here very beautiful quilts and testers of beds finely worked and painted and quilted articles of dress.[19]

One of the most complete descriptions of the vast network of trade from west to east and east to west, that moved about the Eastern seas is given by one Tomé Pires in his *Suma Oriental*. Stationed first in India, then in Malacca, he reported in detail to the King of Portugal, on the Indian ports and on the trade at Malacca, the kinds of merchandise, and whence they came. And here we learn that cloth, beads, golden glassware, and other goods from Venice reach these far parts. Again, "There is no trading place where you do not see Gujarat merchants," and that "The Cambay merchants make Malacca their chief trading centre. . . .Malacca cannot live without Cambay, nor Cambay without Malacca . . ." and of China, "The chief trade from China is raw white silk in large quantities, and loose coloured silks, many in quantity, satins of all colours, damask chequered and enrolados in all colors, taffetas and other thin silk cloths called xaas (sash or shash, for turbans) and many other kinds of cloth;" then follows a long paragraph listing other merchandise and he ends "and porcelain beyond count."[20]

The picture is dizzying, the various races, great variety of materials, the stores of gold and spices, and porcelains and metals moving about in this port-to-port barter, ultimately reaching places as remote from each other as England and China. It is no wonder that the Europeans determined to break in on this wealth. Drake, in his circumnavigation of the globe, on reaching the Moluccas in 1588 is reported as seeing "atendants of a king attired in white lawne of cloth of Calicut" and another "attired after the manner of the Country, but more sumptuously than the rest. From his waste down to the ground was all of cloth of golde and the same very rich," and again in another island, "from the middle downward they wear a pintado of silke, trailing on the ground, in colour as they best like."[21] Of course in the Spanish ships Drake had captured off South America there was "linnen and cloth and fine China-dishes of white earth and great store of China silks, of all of which we took as we listed."[21]

The Factors at Work

Once with a toehold in Surat and another at Bantam in Java, the factors sent out by the English Company grew more active, and their reports to the Company in London or to fellow workers in India or eastward are interesting for the revelation of the spread of the trade they were undertaking, and for the kinds of goods advisable for such and such a spot, or for England; and over and over again what to send, what not to send in trade from England. Often they are amusing, frequently touching.

John Hearne, writing from Bantam in 1608 to the East India Company, is concerned for the movements of two ships, the *Hector* and the *Dragon*. He is urgent that "we might have trade at Surat and Cambaya, to sort ourselves with those sort of cloths that are made in those parts . . ." and adds that "if your Worships do mind, to follow this trade it will be very requisite that 2 ships do go for that place only to buy cloth and calicoes so to bring them hither, to have this place constantly furnished." Then he must report that the *Dragon* was in no shape to go to the Moluccas

> . . . for she complained already in many places, she being a very old ship, also that in those places the worms do consume shipping very much, and finally want of sail for she having few already would, in that voyage, consume almost all her sail and here in these places no canvas is to be had, therefore one hundred pounds more or less, would not be lost in laying it out in spare canvas in such a voyage as this. . . . The point I refer to your Worships consideration it being a principal thing to be regarded in such a voyage as this.

So the *Dragon* was to finish loading with spices and go directly to England. Very respectfully the Directors in London are advised

> The Flemings [i.e., the Dutch] do carry very many Flemish nobles for Banda and those places which do procure them good trade, and if it were worth your Worships liking I do think it very requisite that you would likewise send a reasonable quantity of those nobles to us by the next shipping, for with them we may procure good trade at Banda and also in the Moluccas . . .[22]

This plea for coins ended many a report from the factors over many years.

In 1609 from Surat is dated a long report on the prices of goods in India. This mentions indigo, a most important item of import to England, half a dozen kinds of cotton cloth, and

> If Moorish girdles, Turks and cloaks will yield any profit for Barbary with the former Serrybaff [a kind of cotton] as they seem to me, I pray give advice, they are here in abundance and the great chief merchandise. Pintadoes of all sorts, especially the finest, as it seemeth to me, should yield good profit, I mean such as are for quilts and for fine hangings. . . . Quilts made both of white calicoes and of all sorts of painted stuffs are to be had in abundance, and very reasonable. . . . Calicoes both red and blue are here in abundance, it were requisite to give advice what quantity of them were vendible and what price meetest. . . . To write of clothing for Priaman and Bantam with the Maluccos &c were infinite, they being of so many sorts and of such different prices. . . . But note this, that both in these as also in all other kinds of merchandise, little good will be done unless here be left stock to buy them before shipping come, for our shipping being here they will have double their value, or else will not sell them. They are as 'substill as the Devill' whose limbs I certainly persuade myself they are.

Follows a list of many Eastern goods, chief always "gumlack," then sandalwood, and various kinds of incense, seeds, rice, ginger (always mentioned), drugs of unknown character, cardamoms, benzoin, aloes, dried myrobalams of all sorts (which we shall meet later in the painting of cotton), opium always mentioned, but with the remark that it is so expensive in India; then more drugs and seeds, and finally—

> Goods to be brought from England and vendible in India. . . . Cloth of all kinds of light and pleasant colours, pleasing to the eye as Venice reds, stamels, some few scarlets for presents and also to sell to great men, Popinjay greens of the brightest dye, cinnamon colours, light dove colours, peach colours, silver colours, light yellows with others like, but no dark or sad colours for they are not here vendible; those of the last voyage are yet upon our hands and will not be sold for the monies they cost in England . . .

The list continues through kerseys, baize ("but sayes will not here yield the half they cost in England") quicksilver, lead, tin, vermillion, ivory, red coral, sword blades,

Of new drinking glasses, trenchers for sweetmeats, but especially looking glasses of all sorts and different prices (but not small baubles) some reasonable quantity would be sold to good profit and I veryily suppose that some fair large looking glass would be highly accepted of this King, for he affects not the value of anything but rarity in everything, insomuch that some pretty newfangled toys would give him high content, though their value were small . . .[23]

So they wrote and listed and studied and reported, of what would sell in Priman, or Achin or elsewhere in the Indies, and what in India. The question of the wools was always a matter of argument. For the fact was that English broadcloth was not easy to sell in that hot climate. It served often as gifts and bribes, but in 1615 William Edwards writing to the Company remarked bitterly that he had heard Aldworth (another factor) had urged sending out 1,000 broadcloths and he hopes the letter went astray![24]

As with the Portuguese and their present competitors, the Dutch, their problem was to learn what would sell or be good barter in India, what in the Islands, for spices, where often goods bought from a Chinese junk would go better than English goods. For example, John Jourdain in Jakarta writes a factor in Japan in 1616, "The Gift departed unto England the 22nd December laden with pepper, some cloves, mace nuts and some 50 chests of silk of all sorts. The Lord send her well."[25]

Adam Denton reporting to the East India Company from Patani, 5 October 1614 has information of the trade with the junks, and trouble with the Dutch. At Bantam "Six China Junks came this year with good store of Silk. . . . The English and Dutch at first made a show to join in buying together, but taking no effect each did his best. Mr. Jourdain bought about 60 peculs[26] of raw silk and employed some 60,000 rials in all China commodities beside what Mr. Hall and Mr. Sheppard did each for his particular voyage." This affair was the occasion of much argument between Jourdain and the Dutch, and, as we know, the growing enmity would eventually burst, most unfortunately, into actual battle.

It is impossible to read without compassion, and wonder at their endurance, the reports from these men, often ill, struggling in strange lands against physical difficulties, and coping with the unfamiliar habits of trade; and facing and reporting death of a colleague in a matter-of-fact fashion. As from John Jourdain at Bantam 30 September, 1615, "The 24th of July arrived the Advice and the Attendant. The 6th of August died the General, Nicholas Downton; and the 12th ditto departed the Advice for Japan with some 3,000 rials of Guzeratte cloth . . ."[27]

Some of their difficulties so respectfully reported make amusing reading now. From Adam Denton above quoted,

For want of paper all our books are kept in China paper, having not so much other as to write a letter to your Worships; I therefore entreat your worships to remember us with books, paper and ink of which we have great need, the cockroaches eating the China paper and so dangerous and naught. So my bounden duty finished, submitting myself at your Worships honorable censure and disposing, rest Ever Your Worships Servant to dispose Adam Denton.[28]

Of particular interest to us are the comments on goods to be sought for the home market; among these indigo was of prime importance, and of course the cotton goods. Very early in their letters occur the varieties of the latter.

An example is the long report of 1609 from Surat above quoted in which the writer emphasized the abundance (his favorite word) of various cottons and his belief that pintadoes should yield good profit, such as for quilts and fine hangings; and he craves advice from England concerning what would sell well there. A forward looking merchant!

It is to be understood that in the long, conscientious letters from the factors, either to the London Company or to a chief factor in the Indies, it was the trade for spices in the East, the goods to be bartered, or merchandise procurable, that concerned these hard working factors. From 1619 to 1623 by an arrangement with the Dutch, the English headquarters were at Batavia (formerly Jakarta)[29] and the factors in Masulipatam and Pulicat took instructions from their leaders in Batavia; but the Dutch terms proved too difficult and by 1623 that headquarters had to be given up.

Through these many exchanges between the factors and the Company in London the picture of the trade takes shape. Ship A with wools, metals and money—hopefully much of the last—arrives off Surat. Her cargo is sold and with the money realized, or coin brought as well, the chintz of Gujarat, or Masulipatam if she also goes there, is purchased. Whereupon, Ship A sails for Achin, or Siam, or Bantam, and the India chintz is bartered for pepper and spices, and very likely Chinese goods are procured from a junk. Ship A returns to England and her cargo is sold at India House, headquarters of the East India Company.

Thus the function of the chintz of India was to serve as trade goods for, what at the time was more salable, spice.

Signs of interest in England in the painted cottons, the chintz, emerge slowly through the factors' letters. In 1618 John Browne wrote the London Company from Ahmedabad: "For these quilts party-cullered, we shall by Godes grace make tryall for their provision according to your order in some small quantitie, and for those also of cuttaine (cotton? or half cotton, half silk?) but no great number for that we cannot get taylors enough to work."[30]

The same year, from Agra, Francis Fettiplace wrote the Company that he will order some pintado quilts and is sending samples of some materials.[31]

In 1619 Thomas Kerridge and Thomas Rastell at Surat wrote the Company in a long summary of trade that the Ahmedabad factors were unable to purchase quilts there this year, but will supply some "pintalloe" quilts from other places. Yet later that year the same factors wrote instructions to those at Agra giving them directions for the quilts required:

> . . . some, all of one kind chinte, the lynings and uper parts of one and the same; some of different chintes, yet such as either side may be used; and some to have borders only of different cullers about a covide deep, to hange by the bed side on all sides alike. This last is most used in India, and wee thinke will be most pleasinge to England. . . . They must be a little thicker and stronger sticht than ordinary, for their better lastinge. . . . Lawne quilts we do not conceave soe fitt for England as if they were of semianoe, ambertes or sahume cloth which will be much more lastinge, stichte with birds, beastes or worke very thicke, such as used by the Mores instead of carpetts. Of this sorte there comes, it seemes, from Bengala . . . His Lordship (Sir Thomas Roe?) had three or four which he bought lasker (?) stichte with cullered silke, that will give good contente in England; and we doubt not, by bespeakinge, you will procure them to be made of such sizes as the Companies letter mencion.[32]

This last is what we might call "styling" and, for all the male awkwardness of the language is evidently a response to a request from the English Company.

Considerably later in 1633 one Emanuel Altman is writing from Armagon to Thomas Colley at Petapoli, to have made for him "six very large lansoles well painted with flowers, big enough for an English bed; also two or three pillow beers. . . . Let the 'Lansoles' be 3½ yards or more long, and nearly three broad." In a P.S., Altman acknowledges receipt of two "Chintes" from Colley. Here is evidence of an order to measure for a use in England, and the "chintes" are probably yardage.[33]

Before we leave this running comment on the factors and their labors let us sum up a few points that have been lightly touched: the recurring objection to the amount of wool sent, or the wrong colors; the necessity of providing the right gifts; "toyes and rarities please the King" is a kind of theme song in their reports and when one factor warns that "Bone lace and gloves will not sell," one wonders who in the Company would send out English bobbin lace to India. More serious were the complaints of private trade which began early in letters home; that the "Mariners" and merchants bought goods in India to sell privately in England —thus damaging the Company's monopoly. "Watch the Globe on arrival" warns John Browne in 1617.

All the reports are heavy with trouble with the Dutch, who had by 1610 established factories on the Coromandel Coast, and were extremely successful. Like the English, they needed the superior chintzes of this section to trade for spices. Although the English attempted a certain amount of cooperation in trade, there were always difficulties. One factor writing the Company in 1618 from Petapoli declared: "Theis buter boxes are groane soe insolent that yf they be suffered but a whit longer, they will make claim to the whole of India."[34]

The question of money, the need for coins to be sent them is a constant problem, and comments on the lack were often bitter.

Here we might point out that as early as 1615 the factors became involved in trade between India and Persia. This venture was a picking up of another old commerce. In 1622 the English, encouraged by the Persian ruler Shah Abbas, successfully dislodged the Portuguese from Ormuz, and headquarters were set up at Gombroon on the mainland.

We cannot go on to a discussion of the materials without reference to one frightful year —1631—when western India was devastated by a famine. President Rastell at Surat wrote the Company, "The country being wholy dismantled by drought . . . the poor mechaniques, weavers, washers, dyers, abandoning their habitacions in multitudes, have perished in the feilds for want of food to sustain them."[35]

James Slade, aboard the *Mary* at Swally wrote at length to the Company 9 December 1631 that on arrival they found "the President well but all the merchants in the factory either dead or those living scarcely able to help the Sicke. So that the tymes here are so miserable that never in the memory of man any the like famine and mortality hapened. This that was in a manner the garden of the world is now turned into a wilderness having few or noe men left to manure their ground nor to labor in any profession."[36]

The Materials

The painted cottons which we illustrate here are, with one exception (Plate 1) not styled for use in India. They were made for export to be sold in Holland, England, or France. Their uses in the land of their origin were manifold but different from those of Europe, except for one or two categories. First, of course, was dress material. In India and the islands east of her, the painted cottons, particularly those of the east or Coromandel coast were in demand for clothing. By the late seventeenth century painted cottons were becoming popular in Europe for women's dress, and to a certain extent for men. They were fashionable as dressing gowns: Pepys rented one in which to have his portrait painted. "To Hale's" he wrote on 1, April 1666, "and there sat till almost quite dark upon working my gowne, which I hired to be drawn in."[37]

Other functions shared by Europe and India were the bed covers, the "palempores," and the quilts, though here again European taste soon laid its hand on the Indian fashion. Linschoten reported from Cambay:

> They make also fine coverlets . . . which are very fair and pleasant to the eye, stitched with silke and also of cotton, of all colours and stitchings, pavilions of divers sorts and colours. . . ." And from Bengal he describes a fine cloth made of an "hearbe with which they do most cunningly stitch their coverlets, pavilions, pillows, carpets and mantles . . . and make them with flowers and branches and personages that is wonderful to see and so finely done with cunning workmanshippe that it cannot be mended (equaled) throughout Europe. . . .[38]

This note is to be remembered when considering designs of chintz native to India. Linschoten was traveling there in the last quarter of the sixteenth century, while it was still much under the control of the Portuguese. Many later travelers—English, French, Italian—wrote with enthusiasm of these materials of India. One of the most entertaining and on the whole most rewarding records is that of Jean Baptiste Tavernier who made six voyages to India, as well as to Persia and the Near East. He called himself a jewel merchant and much of his reporting is on stones, but his long descriptions of various kinds of merchandise, from silk to spices, are valuable. His travels were from 1632 to 1667. By this time the Dutch and English were settled in many sections, and he mentions several convivial meetings with both.[39]

As to the customs of use by the Indians, let us point out that any brief examination of Persian or Indian paintings quickly demonstrates that the chair was an almost unknown article. Of course there are beautiful little thrones or platforms or pavilions for the chief personage in a scene, as a prince or a hero. But otherwise it is plain that these people sat upon the ground or floor; and frequently, indoors or out, they are, as Sir Thomas Roe found them, "sitting upon good carpetts." Also we occasionally discover a light colored cloth, patterned, spread between seated figures, on which are dishes of fruit or jars of wine, perhaps[40] and it appears such cloths of figured cotton (our chintz) were used instead of the "good carpet" on which to rest.

Again, in examining the paintings we observe the great rolls or cushions against which various personages lean. They are always of figured material and though no doubt many were of rich embroidery or silk, we would like to believe many were of chintz. It must have been to supply these that Sir Thomas Roe wrote the Company: "Insteade of sweete baggs, rownde cusions gathered like cloked bags, to lean on."

An Italian, Pietro della Valle, arrived in India in 1623 and adds his comments on the dress and customs. [41] Describing the clothing of Mahommedan men, always of white "linnen" which he explains is cotton, he mentions a cassock and long drawers, and sharply observes "tis a piece of gallantry to have it wrinkled in many folds upon the legs. The naked feet are no otherwise confined but in a slipper, and that easie to be pulled off without the help of the hand; the mode being convenient, in regard to the heat of the country and the frequent use of standing and walking upon Tapestry in their chambers." We know certainly that he is not referring to the silk and gold, or wool tapestries of Europe, but to their own floor coverings which were either the woven carpet, or the patterned cottons.

In one of his most interesting articles on the Indian painted cottons, John Irwin, in his study, *Golconda Cotton Paintings of the Early Seventeenth Century*,[42] illustrates two large floor spreads, one in the collection of the Victoria and Albert Museum, the other in the Calico Museum of Textiles, Ahmedabad. These he describes as Indo-Persian in style, dated 1625–1635. The design of the one at the Victoria and Albert Museum is intended to be seen from opposite sides, and consists of boarders showing figures amid foliage, hunting, drinking, or otherwise enjoying life, the trees and plants extending toward the center from each side in a glorious mixture of flowers, foliage, and birds, in shades of red, green, blue, purple, and brown. Many of the flowers or plants exhibit that extravagant character of size, or unreality later to be seen in the palampores made for Europe. Mr. Irwin states that this and the similar piece at Ahmedabad" are perhaps the most beautiful design of all surviving Golconda cotton paintings." Surely in this panel we see plants and flowers drawn with a sureness and gaiety that argue an established style of painting of considerable skill and, in this example, free of the foreign intervention to come.

In the same publication Mr. Irwin illustrates three small covers from the collection of the Metropolitan Museum of Art, New York, and two in the National Museum of India, New Delhi, all of which show adaptation of design from Persian miniatures, and exhibit the small floor spreads in use, the fat cushions on which people are leaning, and as to their costumes such variety of pattern as to make one believe they must be drawn from painted cotton.

A more dramatic use of these materials is described for us by the French doctor, François Bernier, who traveled in India between 1656 and 1668, during the reign of Aurangzeb, and for a short time followed the court on an expedition to Kashmir. The movements of these Mughal emperors were elaborate and luxurious, for they journeyed with all the courtiers, attendants, guards, and the seraglio, employing a system of camps, one of which went ahead of the Emperor and was always in readiness on his arrival. Bernier's description is exact and detailed but too long to quote save for a few references:[43]

The whole of this extensive square is then encompassed with kanates or screens, seven or eight feet in height. . . . The kanates are made of strong cloth lined with printed Indian calico, representing large vases of flowers. The royal entrance, which is in the centre of one of the sides of the square and the flowered calico of which it is composed as well as that which lines the whole exterior face of the square, is of much finer texture and richer than the rest.

And later, of the king's private tents,

which are surrounded by small kanates, of the height of a man, some lined with Maslipatam chintz, painted over with flowers of a hundred different kinds, and others with figured satin, decorated with deep silken fringe.

And of another in this city of tents, The Am-kas,

And the five or six other principal tents are elevated above the rest, as well for the sake of keeping off the heat as that they may be distinguished at a distance. The outside is covered with a strong red cloth, ornamented with large variegated stripes; but the inside is lined with beautiful hand painted chintz manufactured for the purpose at Maslipatam, the ornamentation of which is set off by rich figured satin of various colours, or embroideries of silk, silver and gold, with deep and elegant fringes. Cotton mats, three or four inches in thickness are spread over the whole floor, and these again are covered with a splendid carpet, on which are placed large square brocade cushions to lean upon.

It was perhaps for such a tent lining as described by Bernier that our panel at Plate 1 was made.

It appears that by the middle of the seventeenth century the importance of the chintz in English and Dutch trade was creeping up on the spices. The Dutch success in creating almost a monopoly of the spice trade and in fixing prices at Amsterdam is an interesting commercial experiment, but, involved as the history is with expansion of world trade and a series of European wars, it becomes too long a story for this short article.[44]

Bernier in 1666, in writing a friend in France on the richness of Bengal said—

. . . there is in Bengale such a quantity of cotton and silks that the kingdom may be called the common storehouse for those two kinds of merchandise, not of Hindoustan or the Empire of the Great Mogul only, but of all the neighboring kingdoms, and even of Europe. I have been sometimes amazed at the vast quantity of cotton cloths, of every sort, fine and course, white and coloured, which the Hollanders alone export to different places, especially to Japan and Europe. The English, the Portuguese, and the native merchants deal also in these articles to a considerable extent.[45]

Was it not this year that friend Pepys was sitting for his portrait in London in an "Indian gown" rented for the purpose?

On the Coromandel Coast and in Golconda the Dutch were strong, had organized the production of the painted cottons in methods to produce larger quantities, and on the Coromandel Coast "insisted on the supplies conforming to samples, and thus introduced the idea of specific standardization which was apparently a novelty in this region."[46]

Shortly after his return to France, Bernier wrote a long letter to Colbert, which was included in the publication of his travels and in which he describes the political and financial condition of India in very critical terms. Colbert had founded the Compagnie des Indes Orientales in 1664. Its early years were marked with many difficulties: principally lack of support from the home government. In 1674 a French settlement at Pondicherry was secured, but it was not until 1740 that their trade equalled that of the English settlements. It was, however, from the short-lived French settlement that the two records came describing the technique of painting these cottons, to which we shall presently refer.

The materials illustrated in the catalogue to follow may be said to come from centers of production of the three countries most active in India at the end of the seventeenth century: the English, Dutch, and French. Any examination of the photographs, even without the brilliant colors which were their chief characteristic, convinces the eye that there are here a great mingling of sources of design. No generalizations are safe and one is tempted to lean on the well-worn word "exotic." True, there is a frequent reliance on a tree, often richly blooming with unfamiliar flowers, or happily growing a good many different species from the same branch. Usually the tree grows from a hillock, a little landscape, a mound, some-times, earthy, sometimes stylized in triangle form. About one we sense an air of Chinese line; about another, Persian; or the two mingle, while in others there is obvious adaptation of European motifs, not always clearly understood. One quality is always apparent: the hand of the craftsman, as he plays with the line of a flower's head or vine, is sure, deft, rarely clumsy. Indeed the flowery fantasies of these chintzes would seem evidence of a traditional skill, and, if one may venture an interpretative remark, of a kind of enjoyment in their creation.

Much has been written on the sources of design to be found in Indian chintzes, particularly by John Irwin and Mrs. Katharine B. Brett, in their many articles listed in the bibliography for this study, and most recently in their collaboration, *Origins of Chintz*, published in 1970. Since their studies are authoritative it will be best for the reader if a summary of their conclusions is given at this point.

It is, we hope, clear that the English (and Dutch) interest in India chintzes was at first as barter for pepper and spices. Several of the early records from which we have quoted have emphasized their extensive uses in the East Indies. But we have also tried to indicate, from the same records, that India cottons were valuable as trade goods in the Levant, and Africa, as well as for a certain amount of home consumption.

By the first years of the seventeenth century small quantities of the painted cottons, "pinthathoes," had been imported by merchants in returning spice ships and had aroused attention as curiosities. It would appear that sufficient interest had built up to move the Directors of the East India Company to advise the factors in India, "Those which here-after you shall send we desire may be with more white ground, and the flowers and branch to be in colours in the middle of the quilt as the painter pleases, whereas now most part of your quilts come with sad red grounds which are not equally sorted to please all buyers." Success followed these instructions; the home demand grew, and in 1662, for the first time actual patterns were sent out for the cotton painters to follow.[47]

What were the patterns sent? None, it seems, have survived, and speculation must depend on evidence from the materials surviving. Here again the two writers quoted have contributed many valuable ideas, not to say definite studies! Embroidery designs, which were sold or made professionally from the time of Elizabeth and printed or engraved in the seventeenth century, might well have been the source of many a curled heavy leaf, in the chintzes; flower paintings,[48] wallpaper, particularly after the Chinese papers, were imported into England; and, it is suggested, Flemish verdure tapestries might account for some of the foliage found in the Indian designs. In this connection one is reminded of the request for tapestries from the Emperor Jahangir and his various factotums, and it is tempting to wonder what, beyond cupidity, inspired this desire. Had the more luxurious of the Portuguese rulers imported tapestries in sufficient quantities to inspire interest in India? Albuquerque as he prepared to take Ormuz, in 1514, hung his flagship with figured tapestries from Flanders.[49] It is perhaps a long shot to suppose any cotton painters in seventeenth-century India had been inspired by tapestries imported by Portuguese—but it is permitted to wonder!

As for what further was sent in the way of pattern from England, it appears to this writer that whatever was in vogue at the time would have been considered suitable, and would have been forwarded; this must also have been so in the case of the Dutch company. Thus, we find designs in the chintz based on brocaded silks, English embroideries in crewel work, or French block prints. And if we find an eccentric pattern based on Japanese designs, we may remember the Dutch had trade with that country.

Some paragraphs back we remarked on a traditional skill among cotton painters, and the frequent appearance of a tree growing on a mound. On this as on other points the authors of *Origins of Chintz* are enlightening.[50] The tree is derived from Persian and Indo-Persian painting, and it is not, as we see it in the chintzes, in any way related to the so-called "tree of life," an ancient and different symbol. Taken over from the miniatures, it of course changes under the influence of Western styles; with the tree came the mound or rockery, so often a feature of the Persian art. Often the tree in the Persian version had partly exposed roots; misunderstanding this feature, the cotton painter might show the tree with completely exposed roots, sometimes hung in air above the mound. This misunderstanding of a design occurred when the painters were confronted with some European pattern, completely alien to their experience. To the Persian and Indo-Persian source must be added the Chinese. This entered the consciousness of the Indian in various ways but primarily from the same Persian painting, which itself was influenced by China. We cannot do better on this point than quote directly from the work we have been following: "These Chinese influences, first reaching Western Asia in the wake of the Mongol invasion, continued to fertilize the visual arts of the Islamic world throughout the period with which we are concerned."[51] To this more authoritative theory the present writer would add that in records of many of the early travelers we find reference to the quantity of Chinese porcelain reaching India in trade. Duarte Barbosa, the Portuguese, early in the sixteenth century visited a city he called Reynel, more correctly Rander, near Surat, which he found rich and prosperous from trade with Malacca and China. "The Moors who dwell here are wealthy and distinguished . . . and they have good houses well kept and furnished. They use, in the front room of their houses,

Bill, dated 1701, from John Rudyard and John Jesse to the Duke of Bedford,
for six Indian Callicoe quilts.

to have many shelves all around . . . all filled with fair and rich porcelain of new styles."[52]
To the more obvious contacts with China through trade and the many references in letters
from the factors to Chinese goods taken from the junks, we must add Mr. Irwin's theory of
English Chinoiserie, first made known in his article "Origins of the 'Oriental Style' in English Decorative Art" published in the *Burlington Magazine*, in April 1955. Crudely put, this
fascinating study shows that as England had by the late sixteenth century and early seventeenth developed a Chinoiserie style of her own, its influence was transmitted in patterns
sent by the company to India. In our notes on this Museum's textiles illustrated at Plates
2 and 3, we have commented on the idea.

By 1700 the importation of Indian chintz had become a successful business in England—
too successful according to the woolen and silk manufacturers. France also took fright, and
fearing interference with her famous silk manufacture, enacted in 1786 a prohibition against
the importation of the "indiennes."[53] In 1700 a law was passed in England forbidding the
importation of chintz, but extensive evasion was possible for importation for re-export was
allowed.

The ban was hardly effective, as bills and household inventories would show. In 1701
the Duke of Bedford bought of John Rudyard and John Jesse at Three Kings Within Ludgate,
six Indian Callicoe Quilts at twenty-eight shillings each, which in those days amounted to
eight pounds eight shillings.[54]

Daniel Defoe was one of the most outspoken critics of the East-India Trade, not to say
bitter. His many denunciations provide a picture of the extent to which chintz had become
fashionable. Among other diatribes, he wrote in 1720, "And thus, if there were a Deficiency
in the Number of Wearers, it is made up many other Ways: There are many Thousands of
Women who have two or three several Suits of Callicoe at a Time, for Morning Gowns,
Wrapping Gowns, and in Mantua's, and such like, besides that out of the Number of Yards

calculated by the Commissioner are excluded, the great Quantities used in Furniture, such as Quilts for Beds and Window-Curtains, and the like."[55]

In 1720 England imposed a second ban, forbidding the wearing of chintz, or its use in upholstery or furnishings. The laws were never successful, and there was always Holland to turn to, where no prohibitions had been enacted. Lady Mary Wortley Montagu wrote from the Hague, in 1716, to her friend Jane Smith in England, "If you want any Indian Goodes, here are great Variety of Pennorths and I shall follow your orders with great pleasure and exactness."[56]

That the fashion persisted is shown by an entry in the letters of Henry Purefoy to Anthony Baxter, a London merchant, who wrote in 1735: "If it is in your way to light of a workt chintz for a gown & a petticoat they are generally workt in very fine change stitch & in all colours as chintzes are printed, let us know of it or if not enough for a gown and petticoat enough for a wrapper."[57] The phrase "workt in fine change stitch and in all colours as chintzes are printed" is interesting, bearing out the theory that many embroidered curtains or palampores were taken from the chintz designs. This Museum possesses the back of a lady's gown of the eighteenth century beautifully embroidered on fine cotton in all colours; it would be delightful to find a chintz counterpart.

In 1638 Purefoy wrote the same merchant, "I did write to you once before to know if you could get mee 18 yards of chintz to make window curtains for a drawing room, or something that would suitt workt chairs, workt in shades upon white."[58]

It is needless to multiply examples of its widespread use. Chintz was "in." France, England, Holland, Switzerland—all the countries of Europe—were wearing chintz, decorating with chintz, and the various cotton printing centers were busy adapting the patterns to that business which was to expand during the eighteenth century and into the nineteenth. The designs of the Indian materials kept pace with the changing styles of the eighteenth century and often the Indian chintz appeared more European than Indian. When, for example, the delicate but unreal floral patterns in our patchwork curtains are examined (Plate 14) one wonders whether such flowers were inspired by Pillement or whether that creator of the fantastic had not looked upon the Indian's work and from it developed one of his own devices,[59] rich and strange. Idle speculation.

The trade routes of the chintz did not end in Europe, for in the seventeenth century, we recall, the cheaper cottons were exported to Africa, the Guinea coast, and from there to the West Indies. But the English colonies of North America were to share in the enjoyment of the Indian painted cottons.

The Plantations

Whatever was in fashion in London was desired in the colonies. Anyone familiar with the diaries and letter books of Samuel Sewall of Boston, written toward the end of the seventeenth century, will recall that his many requests to friends or relatives in England reveal, even in so pious a man, this desire to be correct. Indeed "whatever be in fashion" was the plea in letters from the colonists to the homeland until the War for Independence. It is probable that the exportation of Indian cottons to this country began in the late seventeenth century, particularly as in New York the will of Margrita Van Varick, taken in May 1695/1696, listed many Indian materials, as well as objects of Indian make. As Margrita arrived in New York in 1685, and married her husband, rector of a church on Long Island, what more likely than that the Indian materials came to Margrita through the Dutch East India trade? The interesting document containing her will was published by Charles Montgomery in the *Winterthur Newsletter*, number 2, 26 February, 1962 and 26 March, 1962. Several entries of Indian textiles catch the eye: "one Chint flowered carpet; one callico Carpet; a pss. of Chints and remnant of Chints (these two deemed worth leaving to two sons) and again "one Chint carpett, . . . one Chint petticote, one callico wastcote, one Chint ditto . . . seven chints mantells . ." These items are selected from long lists of bequests to various sons and daughters. As there are entries of "East India silver wrought dishes," and "East India silver wrought boxes," as well as an "East India Cabinet with ebony feet wrought," plainly we have here evidence of the importation and use of India materials on these shores in the late seventeenth century.

Happily for our subject, the English preserve the documents of their history and trade with such admirable care. In the Public Records Office in London are held many large volumes of tax records, listing annual exports, among them the exports to the "plantations." The goods, a surprising variety, are listed in alphabetical order, for each year, and it will so happen that "Grocry currants" may fall in line next to "Callico." They are also written, across the big pages, to show quantities, values, and total costs. The lists of exports are grouped according to the plantations to which they are shipped, London to New England, London to New York, London to Pennsylvania, and London to Maryland and Virginia. The latter pair of plantations usually drew a fair amount of Indian textile material. However, the exportation of the Indian cottons was pretty well spread among coastal settlements in the eighteenth century. Reading a photostat of a page for London to New England (Customs 3/50) 1749 to 1750, we observe a list of twenty-three textiles, all but three of which are surely Indian, beginning with "Bandannoes" and ending with "Palampores." Of the last named there were 19, of Chintz 280 pieces, of ginghams 164, and of nicannees 190 pieces.[60]

While the evidence from the English records is valuable, the exportation to the colonies is to be found among many sources on our side of the Atlantic; the advertisements in newspapers are the most obvious: From the *Providence Gazette*, 21 January, 1764, "Smith and

Where Exp.d and fro' whence	For. Merchan.dz Out of Time?	Eng. Ships	For. Ships	Estimate of the Value in England.	Amount of the value £ s d
From London To New England	Linen Russia	635.1.20		At 6.10 q 8lb	4.130 4 2
	Oyl Linseed	2 Gall.ns		At 27 to 30 Ton.	.. 4 6
	Sallet	7.		At 3.6 to 5.6 Gall.n	1 11 6
	Paper Ordin.y	10 Reams		At 4.6 to 6.6 Ream	2 15 ..
	Pastboards	2.160 N.o		At 20 to 24 m	2 7 6
	Salt Petre	6.0.0		At 36.6 to 38 q	9 6 3
	Steel	90.0.0		At 38 to 40 q	175 10 ..
	Bandannoes	336 p.s		At	672 .. ..
	Beutapauts	501.		At	626 5 ..
	Carradarees	10.		At	9 .. ..
	Chelloes	25.		At	21 5 ..
	Cherconees	1.		At	1 2 ..
	Chillaes	18.		At	10 16 ..
	China Ware	16.		At	1 5 3
	Chints	280.		At	371 .. ..
	Cushtaes	16.		At	12 .. ..
	Damasks	3.		At	10 10 ..
	Dissooksoys	11.		At	27 10 ..
	Dunadiks	74.		At	92 10 ..
	Elatches	6.		At	4 16 ..
	Ginghams	161.		At	221 8 ..
	Gorgoroons	10.		At	32 10 ..
	Goshees	20.		At	7 .. ..
	Handkf.s Silk	89.		At	111 5 ..
	Silmills	3.		At	3 6 ..
	Lemonees	32.		At	48 .. ..
	Niccanees	190.		At	142 10 ..
	Padusoys	10.		At	32 10 ..
	Palampores	19.		At	28 10 ..
	Poisees	15.		At	135 .. ..

Page from Tax Records, 1749–1750. Exports London to New England. Public Records Office, London, by Permission of H.M. Stationery Office.

Sabin at the Sultan's Head, near Great Bridge, hereby inform their customers, that they have just received a fresh supply of European and East India Goods . . . etc." From the *Providence Gazette* and *Country Journal*, 18 October, 1766, Samuel Nightengale, has a large assortment of English, India and West India Goods. Thus they continue, and often end, as James Green, 8 November, 1766 with the assurance of a supply of "choice Bohea and Green Tea, by the dozen or smaller quantity; the best French indigo, raisins, currants, spices. . ."

A patient digger in records of historical societies, particularly in port cities, will encounter proof of the arrival of India goods. In the Rhode Island Historical Society the papers of such prosperous merchants as Christopher Champlin, or Godfrey Malbone (or Mallbone) often include ships' invoices where lists of bales, bundles, boxes, trunks of India goods occur. Various records in the New York Historical Society mention India chintz and other India cottons. To be sure in the early papers the transactions are small, but the Peter Jay Daybook, 1734–1748, reports: "35 pieces of Chintz from John Isles of Bristol, consigned to John Savage and Co. merchants, Sloop Rebecca for So. Carolina." The account book of Oliver Wolcott, volume 1, 1804–1810, indicates direct transactions with Calcutta and lists ample sales of chintzes, as 80 pieces, or 10 bales, to various merchants.

One of the most useful sources is contained in the *Beekman Mercantile Papers*, published by the New York Historical Society, 1956. James Beekman was a most successful dealer in dry goods and his correspondence with various merchants in England, his long lists of goods ordered, are funds of information to anyone concerned with the subject of textiles and the names of the materials are frequently a torment. Beekman did much business with a firm of Pomeroy and Streatfeild in London and through their letters to him we glimpse the troubles with orders from India in the mid-eighteenth century. "Our disappointment of an East India sale in March last," they wrote 20, August 1756 "which we always used to have, and out of which we were always supplied with Callicoes to print in the summer season, hath rendered it impossible to conform to Your order for quantity . . ."[61] In October 1757, there was more trouble, "Our East India Company not having had any sale, for twelve months have put it out of our power to supplie You with the quantity of East India goods You wrote for, and have been obliged to reduce the orders of all our friends for that commodity . . ."[62]

The town of Salem in Massachussetts is delightful in early summer. Quite aside from the interest of the Peabody Museum and the Essex Institute, there are still the handsome houses of the eighteenth century, and the sea, and somehow the maritime history of Salem is with you there.

Walk down Derby Street, with the harbor to your right, and you come to a tall red brick building, the old Custom House, from the window of which you look out on the harbor and the long wharf, now a park, once busy with the maritime activities of Elias Hasket Derby's pursuits. A short distance beyond the Custom House stands the handsome Derby House, and here this writer found on a bed, in what today would be called "the master bedroom," a handsome palampore. This house and the Custom House are administered by the National Park Service. At the Custom House the manager kindly produced records of the palampore's history. Captain Gamaliel Hodges, connected with the Derby shipping firm, brought the palampore from India and gave it to his daughter, Mrs. George Choate. Her grandaughter, Miss Mabel Choate, presented the palampore to a friend in Salem who was active in the restoration of some of Salem's historic houses. Unfortunately no photographs are available. From the store of records in the Custom House, however, the manager provided us with photocopies of two ships' manifests trading with Calcutta in 1801 and 1802. These list, in addition to large quantities of sugar and hides, a great number of bales, boxes, trunks of piece goods, as, in the language of trade, the India cottons were called.

Salem, after the Revolution, became an exciting center for trade to the east and once again pepper was the lure. It is no part of this study to recount events of the years when Salem became the "world emporium for pepper."[63] But it is surprising to realize that by 1791 American seamen were trading at Achin, that spot on the northwest coast of Sumatra where the first East India Company touched in 1601. Though a trade in cotton with Calcutta developed from Salem, it is probable that the palampores found there, one of which is illustrated, came to Salem with the sea captains as gifts.

TECHNICAL DESCRIPTION

The Making of the Chintzes

We have called them painted cottons, and in truth it is hard to think of another expression but actually what was painted on the cloth was the outline of a design, and the mordants required to develop a color. Our painted cottons are really decorated in an elaborate, lengthy system of mordant dyeing, combined with resist techniques.

The system must have been of great antiquity. The *Periplus* mentions in many places the importation of cottons from India, and in museum collections are found the fragments of resist printing in blue or in dull red, which have been discovered in the ruins of Fostat, the old Cairo. Pfister has published interesting material on these cottons, and dates many of them from the fourteenth century though it is possible recent research might not agree with his attribution, finding many of them later. They are interesting examples of trade goods and the Cooper-Hewitt Museum has a small collection of fifteen pieces.

For the method of painting and dyeing our chintzes, we may refer to two studies. One, first published in Baker's *Calico Painting and Printing in the East Indies in the 17th and 18th Centuries*, was the letter from Father Coeurdoux, a Jesuit missionary in India, to his superior in Paris in 1742, and again printed with a letter dated 1747 in the *Journal of Indian Textile History*, number III, 1957, with scholarly notes by Paul Schwartz.[64] The second source, also French, is a translation of the Beaulieu Manuscript, circa 1734, and published by Paul Schwartz with notes and illustrations in color, in the *Journal of Indian Textile History*, number II, 1956. Beaulieu, employed by the Compagnie des Indes, was first a midshipman then lieutenant in the Navy, and in the course of one of his sojourns in India had the samples made as described in the manuscript.

Both these letters or reports are of great interest, as they illustrate the long, patient, detailed labor covering days and weeks which the making of the painted cottons involved. One thing is obvious: the system was completely empiric.

Before launching into an explanation of the Indian process of painting cotton, it should be made clear that block printing on cotton was carried out in India[65] and was frequently mentioned by company agents and travelers, but usually with the reservation in favor of the painted cotton as finer. It is the latter only with which we are concerned, and which we illustrate.

A mordant, according to Webster's Dictionary is "Any substance which, by combining with a dyestuff to form an insoluble compound or lake, serves to produce a fixed color in a textile fiber, in leather, etc." An older definition, from a nineteenth-century writer phrases it thus: "A mordant is a substance which can exert an affinity for the fibrous material to which it is applied and which possesses at the same time an attraction for coloring matters. It is necessary that it should possess these double properties or it cannot be considered as a mordant. Mordants are not very numerous and may be divided into mordants proper and mordants of a dubious nature: the first class consisting of those metallic salts whose oxides seem to effect an intimate chemical union with the fibre and coloring matter. . . ."[66] The Indian craftsman would not have used such elegant circumlocutions. He had learned the use of mordants, somehow, by experience; or his great, great grandfather had passed down the knowledge, in his caste.

Any reader who has time to look up the famous letter from Father Coeurdoux, or the translation of the Beaulieu Manuscript by Paul Schwartz as noted above, is urged to do so, as the descriptions of the process are picturesque, and, to the mind of the present, somewhat astonishing.

To begin with, the work was done out-of-doors, preferably beside a pool or river, as the water of the pool was frequently used. We read too, in records of the English factors, that the work was done by very poor men, and sometimes children, and carried out in a kind of family system, where the work was divided within a group. And, although this is not made clear in the Beaulieu Manuscript, dyeing in indigo was the work of a separate caste, and at one point in the long process the material was handed over to the indigo dyer, by the painter. This is noted in the letter from Father Coeurdoux.

Very roughly summarized this was the process described in the Beaulieu Manuscript. The cloth was partially bleached, then impregnated with a liquor made of Buffalo milk and myrobolans. The rather sticky qualities of these substances would prevent the mordants from running. Many washings, dryings, and beatings took place. A design on paper was pricked and pounced on the cloth with powdered charcoal just as an embroideress does today. Next came the preparation of mordants. An iron mordant was made (it seems to have taken three days) by covering vitriolic stones (or iron fragments), with palm wine and allowing it to sour. With this the painter traced or outlined all the parts of the design that were to be blue, green, or violet. This produced a first faint outline, in black.

A mordant for red was prepared with a liquor containing color from Sapan wood and alum. With this the painter traced all the parts to be red. Also he shaded all the parts that were to be red and black, respectively.

The red dye from chay root was now prepared. The cloth was immersed in the dye, boiled over a moderate fire, left to cool, then removed and washed in fresh water. The dyeing in chay blackened the lines already black and developed the reds.

At this point the ground had acquired a rather dirty color, and a long cleansing process was used, of soaking in water containing the dung of kids, much airing on the edge of the pond, sprinkling with water from the pool, a final washing in water of the pond and drying. This operation (which took four days) served to bleach the ground.

A washing in rice water followed and beating against a tree trunk.

Next the cloth was prepared for the indigo dyeing. With molten wax the painter traced the tiny lines that were to remain white on blue. The whole design was outlined with the wax, then he covered with wax all parts of the cloth that were not to be blue in the final design. (If the reader at this point will consider what this process involved in dyeing a big palampore, he may look back with increased respect on these craftsmen.) Indigo requires no mordant—will not work with a mordant—so the resist process was necessary.

After dyeing in indigo the wax was removed in hot water, after which a dunging process and drying in the sun followed, which seems to have taken three days. There follows much detail about the streaking of fine details in the flowers, the preparation of a mordant for yellow from alum and Terramerita (tumeric) with which the parts to be yellow were painted.

Next came a second dyeing in chay-root, followed by many washings, dunging, and final washings in clear water. This cleansing was necessary, to clear the ground of excess red dye.

The last process is to produce green or yellow. (Green, until the early nineteenth century was produced by applying yellow over blue.)

Cadouca, myrobolan and chay-root were combined in a liquid which was heated and with it the painter covered all the parts that were to be green or yellow.

A specially prepared washing liquid was made; the cloth, now completely dyed, was given a final cleansing, airing, sprinkling with water from the pool, and beating.

Returning to our nineteenth-century writer, let us hear his explanation:

> The shades of color which any dyewood can give differ for each mordant and for various strengths of the same mordant; the same coloring matter yielding shades which appear quite opposite in their nature, as for example, madder which with alumina mordants give pink; with strong, red; with weak iron mordants, lilac or violet; and with strong, black colors; while a mixture of iron and alumina mordants yields various shades of chocolate. And these colors are undoubtedly derived or derivable from one single coloring matter. The power of the mordant is therefore very great in influencing the shades.

Chay, the famous red dye of the Coromandel coast, is the equivalent of madder.

A glazed surface is found on many of the Indian chintzes, notably in this Museum's collection, the Ashburnham curtain, Plate 2, and there are remains of a glaze on other pieces. The finishing process which produced the glaze consisted of starching, by employing rice, beetling and chanking, that is a rubbing of the surface with a shell until a high polish was produced.[67]

Those familiar with the history of cotton printing in Europe, in the eighteenth century will recognize, in this outline of the Indian method, several procedures followed in Europe. There was the devotion to the bank of a pool or stream, the sprinkling and airing on its bank. The French perhaps preferred the river of running water. The cleansing or bleaching in a liquid containing animal dung was used throughout the eighteenth century and well into the nineteenth. As we see from the quotation given above alum and iron were basic as mordants.

The process described in the Beaulieu Manuscript took twenty-six days, according to this writer's count, but the decoration of a large palampore, or a curtain, would have taken much longer, depending upon the character of the design, the number of workers employed, and other local conditions. Tavernier, in his useful comments on Indian textiles, has this to say of the chintz: "The chites or painted cotton cloths which are called calmendar, that is to say, painted with a brush, are made in the Kingdom of Golconda, and particularly in the neighborhood of Masulipatam; but the quantity turned out is so small that when one makes requisition on all the workers who manufacture these cotton cloths it is with difficulty that he can obtain as much as three bales."[68] Letters from the various factors bear out this remark of Tavernier's, and complaints of finding painters, of checking up on their work, of meeting requirements of the company, are frequent. The poverty of the workmen, and oppressive conditions of Indian government, added to difficulties; funds were often advanced to them. Both the Dutch and English factors frequently found it advisable to persuade workers to leave their village and move to a settlement near a factory of one or the other.

We noted earlier in this description of the making that children were sometimes employed. In the account by Father Coeurdoux (which incidentally is more detailed than that by Beaulieu), he tells us, in connection with the application of red to the design: "The painting in red is usually done by children, as this kind of work is less strenuous, unless a more perfect work should be wanted."[69] There was another witness to this statement: John Fryer, M. D. Cambridge and Fellow of the Royal Society, as he tells us on the title page of his book of travels,[70] which were begun in 1672 and finished in 1681, visited Masulipatam and reported thus on "Their Craftiness and Skill in Staining Calicuts (calico) . . . having an accomplishment in the Art of Staining Calicuts here beyond any other place in the East-Indies (for that they are upon washing rather clearer and livelier than at first, and this it is that makes this Port so much frequented) which is painted with the Pencil by little Children as well as elder grown, they stretching the Pieces on the ground, and sitting upon them, run them over with a dexterity and exactness peculiar to themselves." Perhaps one should not question the observation of a Fellow of the Royal Society, but when the intricacy of some of the designs is considered, it is perhaps permitted to wonder that even the "elder grown" could accomplish such painting.

Before we leave this section on the making of the chintz we should pay a little attention to the cottons used for the grounds of the chintz painting. The variety of the Indian cottons was enormous, and the widths of weaving varied also, as well as the quality, depending on the ultimate use. The cottons in the Museum's collection are all plain weave, and of several widths.

There are two surprisingly wide, one at Plate 20 the other at Plate 10 being 7 feet 9 inches and 8 feet 8¾ inches respectively. The average width seems to have been 36, or 40 to 45 inches.

Many of the early travelers were rather scornful of the Indian's gifts, maintaining that he could only copy a design, not create one. Certainly we have seen that after the chintz became fashionable in England and all over Europe the designs were indeed "thick o'erlaid" with layers of European influence. Nevertheless the Dutch and the English found existing and available for their exploitation an extraordinary technique. The Indian's tools were of the simplest, the "pencils" being a stick of bamboo with a bit of cloth caught in a cleft at its end; or of iron with a ball of hair in a loop at the end—this last for the putting on of hot wax.[71] Their mordants and their colors came from the forests and fields around them, or nearby regions. Yet with these simple supplies and their native traditional skill they created the painted cottons that, slowly entering the European world, stimulated a wholly new textile industry. The chintzes left to us, frail and faded though some are, may still be enjoyed as examples of a disappearing artistic endeavor.

Notes

1. William Shakespeare, *The Merchant of Venice*, Act I, Scene 3.

2. Frederic Rosengarten, Jr., *The Book of Spices*, pages 47, 48.

3. *The Periplus of the Erythraean Sea*, pages 44, 45, paragraph 56.

4. Rosengarten, *The Book of Spices*, pages 47, 48.

5. John Bruce, *Annals of the Honorable East India Company*, 1810, I, page 112.

6. *Purchas His Pilgrimes*, II, page 364.

7. George B. Parks, *Richard Hakluyt and the English Voyages*, pages 152–160.

8. Ralph Fitch, *Hakluyt, Principal Navigations and Voyages*, page 491.

9. Caesar Frederick (Frederici), *Hakluyt, Principal Navigations and Voyages* (II. 1. 237), page 427.

10. C. Northcote Parkinson, *Trade in the Eastern Seas 1793–1813*, page 69.

11. John Huyghen van Linschoten, *The Voyages to the East Indies*, page 40.

12. *East Indian Trade*, Article: *A True and Large Discourse of the Whole Fleete of Ships Set Forth the 20th of Aprill 1601 by the Governours and Assistants of the East Indian Merchants in London, to the East Indies*, pages 5, 31–34.

13. David Hannay, *The Great Chartered Companies*, pages 73–113.

14. John Stow, *Annals, or a Generall Chronicle of England 1631*, page 13.

15. *The Embassy of Sir Thomas Roe to India 1615–1619*, edited by Sir William Foster, pages 31–35.

16. Roe, *Embassy*, page 181.

17. Roe, *Embassy*, pages 458–460.

18. *The Travels of Ludovico di Varthema*, edited by George Percy Badger, page 212.

19. *The Book of Duarte Barbosa*, I, pages 141–142.

20. *The Suma Oriental of Tomé Pires*, translated by Armando Cortesão, I, pages 45, 125; II, page 269.

21. *Drake's Circumnavigation of the Globe, Hakluyt's Voyages*, edited by Erwin Blacker, pages 236, 238, 241, 249

Linnen: Is often used in the old records when cotton was actually the material seen. Until the travelers became more familiar with cotton, linen was a generic term to include both materials, often occurring in English tax records of the eighteenth century.

22. *Letters Received by the East India Company from Their Servants in the East, 1602–1613*, edited by Frederick C. Danvers, Letter 8, pages 18 19.

23. *Letters Received, 1602–1613*, Volume I, Letter 11, page 28.

24. *Letters Received, 1613–1615*, Volume II, page 154 (Edwards).

25. *Letters Received, 1615*, Volume III, page 112 (John Jourdain to Japan).

26. *Letters Received, 1613–1615*, Volume II, page 118 (Adam Denton).

27. *Letters Received, 1615*, Volume III, page 170 (Jourdain at Bantam).

28. *Letters Received, 1613–1615*, Volume II, page 129 (Denton).

29. *English Factories in India 1622–1623*, page xxxv.

30. *English Factories . . . 1618–1621*, page 10.

31. *English Factories . . . 1618–1621*, pages 46, 47.

32. *English Factories . . . 1618–1621*, pages 84, 85.

33. *English Factories . . . 1630–1633*, pages 123, 124.

34. *English Factories . . . 1618–1621*, page 48.

35. *English Factories . . . 1630–1633*, page 122.

36. *English Factories . . . 1630–1633*, page 178.

37. *Diary and Correspondence of Samuel Pepys*, II, page 366.

38. *Voyage of John Huyghen van Linschoten to the East Indies*, pages 61, 95 *et seq.*

39. Jean Baptiste Tavernier, *Travels in India*, translated by V. Ball, edited by William Crooke, London, 1925, Volume I, Book I, Chapter VIII, page 107.

40. B. W. Robinson, *Persian Miniature Painting*, Plates 22, 27.

41. W. G. Archer, *Indian Painting in Bundi and Kotah*, Plate 26.
Pietro della Valle, *Travels in India*, I, page 41f.

42. John Irwin, *Golconda Cotton Painting of the Early Seventeenth Century*, Lalit Kalā, No. 5, April 1959.

43. François Bernier, *Travels in the Mogul Empire*, pages 360–363.

44. Kristof Glamann, *Dutch Asiatic Trade 1620–1640*, pages 91–109.

45. Bernier, *Travels*, page 439.

46. Raychaudhuri, *Jan Company in Coromandel 1605–1690*, page 145.

47. John Irwin and Katharine B. Brett, *Origins of Chintz*, pages 3, 4.

48. Katharine B. Brett, *An English Source of Indian Chintz Design*, Journal of Indian Textile History, No. 1, 1955.

49. John Dos Passos, *The Portugal Story*, page 250.

50. Irwin and Brett, *Origins of Chintz*, page 17.

51. Irwin and Brett, *Origins of Chintz*, page 18.

52. The Book of Duarte Barbosa, I, pages 146–148.

53. Irwin and Brett, *Origins of Chintz*, pages 5, 6.

54. Facsimile bill, Woburn Abbey, Duke of Bedford.

55. Daniel Defoe, *The Trade to India Critically and Calmly Considered*, London, 1720, page 30.

56. *The Complete Letters of Lady Mary Wortley Montagu*, Oxford, 1966, volume 1, page 251.

57. Elizabeth Purefoy, *The Purefoy Letters, 1735–1753*, London, 1931, page 101, Letter 163.

58. Ibid., page 104, Letter 168.

59. Jean Pillement, *Fleurs, Oiseaux et Fantasies*, Paris, H. Ernst, 1924.

60. Public Records Office (Customs 3/50) 1749–1750. For lists of Indian textile names, consult those given in the *Journal of Indian Textile History*, number I, 1955, pages 25–30; number II, 1956, pages 40–42.

61. *Beekman Mercantile Papers*, 1746–1749. 3 volumes. New York Historical Society, New York, 1956, volume II, page 630.

62. Ibid., page 635.

63. Samuel Eliot Morison. *The Maritime History of Massachusetts 1783–1860*, Boston, 1921, pages 90–91.

64. For a description of cotton printing in India see "L'Impression sur coton à Ahmedabad (Inde) en 1678 d'après un manuscrit inedit de la Bibliothèque Nationale à Paris" by Paul R. Schwartz in *Extraite de la Société Industrielle de Mulhouse*.

65. O'Neill, Charles. *A Dictionary of Dyeing and Calico Printing*. Philadelphia, 1869, page 350.

66. Ibid., page 352.

67. See "Roxburgh Account of Indian Cotton Painting, 1795" by Paul R. Schwartz in *Journal of Indian Textile History*, No. IV, 1959, page 54.

68. Jean Baptiste Tavernier, *Travels in India*, translated by V. Ball, London, 1925, volume II, page 4.

69. Letter from Father Coeurdoux in "French Documents on Indian Cotton Painting" by Paul R. Schwartz in *Journal of Indian Textile History*, number III, 1957, page 32.

70. John Fryer, *A New Account of East-India and Persia*, London, R. Chiswell, 1698, page 31.

71. Letter from Father Coeurdoux, "French Documents," by Paul R. Schwartz, p. 32. For illustrations of these tools, see W. S. Hadaway, *Cotton Painting and Printing in the Madras Presidency*, Madras, 1917, page 28.

CATALOGUE

All of the materials illustrated are Indian, made, with two exceptions, in the technique called painted; and, with one exception (Plate 1), all were made for export. Two embroidered palampores are illustrated, one from this Museum's collection, one from the Museum of Fine Arts, Boston.

The last five photographs are of examples in other collections. Each has a "family history," that is, each is known to have been imported by or to have been used by a given family and its descendants. They are included to illustrate the fact that Indian chintzes were imported by the colonies throughout the eighteenth century, and, after the War for Independence, into the first half of the nineteenth century.

That most sympathetic and cheerful of the English travelers in India, Peter Mundy, paid attention to the natural world around him as he journeyed. Somewhat wistfully he remarked as he left Agra "Heere we had also very good redd roses and white, but the latter excelled in smell" Most seriously he devoted time to a long report on the products of India, and after the trees and fruits come the flowers: "Roses, Jasmines, French marigolds, poppees and other sorts many, especially two, the one called Kheera (the sweet scented pandanus) and the other Chambelee (jasmine grandifloram) as big as a prettie Tewlipp, have couller and smell like a wall jelly flower (gilly flower) Theis growe on Trees as does many others."

In spite of this guidance from the traveler of 1630, we turned to botanists and naturalists, just in case we overlooked a "pretty Tewlipp" which by another name smells so sweet. We have to thank Dr. Wallace Ernst and Dr. Robert Read of the Smithsonian Institution and Miss Carol Woodward for the indentification of a few among the many floral fantasies in the chintz designs, though the general opinion was that the intention of the painters was more to produce a design than a botanical drawing. For the many birds among the flowering trees we were happy to receive the help of Mr. S. Dillon Ripley; and to all we here extend our thanks.

1 PANEL, probably a tent lining; cotton, painted and dyed; Golconda, second half seventeenth century
L. 6 feet 9¼ inches   W. 3 feet 2 inches
Purchased, Au Panier Fleuri Fund   *Acc. no. 1952-111-1*

Colors: two reds, two blues, yellow, green, dull violet, brown.

Design: Architectural form, characteristic of Islamic art, a pointed arch within a perpendicular frame, suggesting the mihrab or prayer niche. Within this frame a symmetrical, balanced pattern shows a slender vase, from which spring branches ending in blossoms; a second slender vase emerging from the first, holds a second cluster of flowers, which almost touch the curved top of the arch. At the base, the vase is supported on a rudimentary hillock, at either side of the vase grow long pointed leaves, and at either corner rise slender branches, from similar small mounds, on which appear fruits (or seed pods?) and flowers. The background color is a dark reddish brown, and on this the main design is enlivened by a secondary pattern of many small leaf sprays or curling waves, reserved in the white of the cloth, which appear throughout among the branches. The vase shape is in red and yellow diamond pattern, the second vase or stem is brown dotted in white; flowers a strong red with much interior delineation of form.

The frame of the mihrab is a narrow red band which surrounds it, base, sides and curved top, and carries a small pattern in brown, yellow, and white. At either side, beyond this red frame is a second narrow border on yellow with small vine and flower-head pattern, which leads up into the spandrels, also yellow, above the pointed arch, where a matching vine design appears on either side of the tip of the arch. A curved segment of a pointed oval closes either side of the spandrels. Across the bottom of the panel runs a border decorated with crosses alternating with diamond shapes, within each of which are stylized patterns. The same border crosses the top of the panel above the spandrels, and above that appear on white ground a row of small iris, or crocus flowers. The curved segment of a pointed oval appearing on either side of the spandrel suggests that this panel was part of a series.

The general color effect is rich and varied with reds, greens, sky blue, dull yellow, orange, and a plum color, and is much lightened by the small reserve pattern on the dark background. This is perhaps the sort of painted cotton which, making its way to England earlier in the seventeenth century, moved the Directors of the East India Company to inveigh against "your sad red grounds." The panel was probably made for a tent lining, such as Dr. Bernier observed with such pleasure in the camp of the Emperor Aurangzeb, descriptions of which were quoted earlier.

The design is Indo-Persian, traditional, and might be compared with patterns in wall tiles, or small Persian carpets. See Grousset, *Civilizations of the East*, figures 156, 167, and 288. See also Seherr-Thoss, *Design and Color in Islamic Architecture: Afghanistan, Iran, Turkey*, plates 62, 63, 89, 129.

This panel was formerly in the collection of Nasli Heeramaneck. His information accompanying its acquisition by the Cooper-Hewitt Museum was that it came from the Palace of Amber.

Published: Jean E. Mailey, "Indian Textiles in the Museum's Collection," *Chronicle of the Cooper Union Museum*, volume 2, number 5, pages 138–139, figures 2 and 3.

Reproduced: Marion Downer, *The Story of Design*, New York, Lothrop Lee and Shepard, 1963.

2   HANGING, cotton, painted and dyed; Western India, late seventeenth century
L. 9 feet 10 inches   w. 8 feet 2 inches
Purchased, Au Panier Fleuri Fund   *Acc. no. 1953–123–1*

Curtain consists of two full breadths, 36 inches wide, and narrow part-breadth, 15½ inches wide.

Colors: two reds, blue, yellow, plum color, reddish brown, and black. Outlines black and red. The general effect is of reds and greens with much shading, touches of light blue, violet, plum color, and light brown at base.

Design: consists of a series of flowering branches, or slender trees, crossed by shorter stalk at base, rising from an exaggeratedly curving rockery, of Chinoiserie character, in which appear animals and humans. From the trees spring a variety of large flowers, many 6 inches wide, unrelated in species; sprays of smaller flowers blossom on lesser branches; leaves mostly heavily curved and notched; butterflies and insects fly about, and birds (peacocks, pheasants, and parakeets) perch on branches or fly among them. Among the flowers a carnation is recognizable, and one heavy flower—possibly a lotus.

Among the inhabitants of the rocky landscape at the base, one is a shepherd in pointed hat with crook over shoulder, blowing a horn to gather his sheep to safety; another, a hunter with round hat and bearing a spear(?) peers from behind a hillock, while below, dogs pursue a leopard; above appears a similar figure with spear or stick, and on top of a rock is seen another man with pointed cap adorned with a feather. There are stags, goats, a leopard, and rabbits huddled in a startled attitude, with pursuing dogs moving in and out of the rockery. The composition of this section, whatever its origin, suggests a hunting scene, such as one sometimes finds in English crewel embroidery, or in tapestry.

Painting: The technique is elaborate—much shading in the big flowers, with two and three shades of red, or two and three colors, as red, light blue and faded violet, with green for the stem. There is much veining; all leaves have interior patterns and are in darker and lighter greens; several of the heavy curled leaves have red centers, dotted lighter and darker. Birds are in shades of red or green in plumage, with feather marking indicated.

The hillocks in the landscape are light brown with darker brown outlines. The men are in red, with patterning suggested on their clothes by shading. Animals are red with darker markings or white spots.

The curtain would appear to have been used, as it is lined with pale blue Chinese damask, contemporary with the chintz; sides and bottom are bound with typical twill curtain binding.

History: This curtain and an embroidered palampore (1953–123–2) described in the following pages, are part of a lot of materials formerly in the collection of Ashburnham House, Sussex, England. They are now divided between the Victoria and Albert Museum, London, the Boston Museum of Fine Arts, and the Cooper-Hewitt Museum.

These materials have been most thoroughly studied by John Irwin and his findings published. He has shown us that the chintz curtains and embroidered pieces were made from

the same pricked design or stencil; and that it was probably a printed design for embroidery sent out from England from which the craftsmen worked. Further evidence of such an English source is that the Boston Museum of Fine Arts possesses an embroidered border in crewels, in the same design as that of the rockery at the bottom of the curtain. As to the Chinoiserie style, Mr. Irwin's opinion is that an early interest in things Chinese (late sixteenth to early seventeenth century) had produced an English style of Chinoiserie which was carried to India in patterns sent out, and so contributed to the fantasy we behold. For this conclusion see article referred to below in the *Burlington Magazine*.

Bibliography: John Irwin; "The Commercial Embroidery of Gujerat in the Seventeenth Century," *Journal of Indian Society of Oriental Art*, volume XVII, 1949, pages 51–56, plate ix. "Origins of the 'Oriental Style' in English Decorative Art," *The Burlington Magazine*, volume XCVII, number 625, April 1955, pages 106–114, plate 11. "Origins of Chintz" by John Irwin and K. B. Brett, 1970, pages 45–46. The two examples in the Boston Museum of Fine Arts have been published by Gertrude Townsend in "Painted Cottons and Embroideries," *Bulletin of the Museum of Fine Arts*, volume LII, number 290, pages 100–104. Boston, December 1954.

Illustrated and noted: Alice Beer, "Why Textiles?" *Chronicle of the Cooper Union Museum*, volume 2, number 7, June 1955, page 213, figure 20.

Exhibited: Royal Ontario Museum, "Origins of Chintz" April 7–May 24, 1970

detail of lining

detail

3 PALAMPORE, cotton, embroidered in silk chain stitch; Western India, late
seventeenth century
L. 9 feet 4 inches w. 8 feet 7 inches
Purchased, Au Panier Fleuri Fund   *Acc. no. 1953–123–2*

This piece is a companion to chintz curtain 1953–123–1 and is part of the lot of materials from Ashburnham House, Sussex. It is of fine cream colored cotton, worked in brilliant
silk chain stitch.

Colors: three reds, violet, pale gray-violet, two blues, yellow; outlines dark brown.

Design: basically the same as that of the chintz curtain, slender flowering trees rising
from a rocky foreground with men and animals appearing there, except that this design is
shown at the bottom of the cover and in reverse at the top; center, a medallion, filled with a
pattern of a fine flowering vine and framing a pair of flying birds; a corner motif is treated
similarly, but with a single bird. A wide border, 17 inches, is decorated with design of large
flowering vine, and guard borders of smaller vine.

The design in the embroidered cover appears simplified and bolder than in chintz.
Large red flowers are outlined in yellow; yellow wings of the big birds outlined in green,
dark body outlined in red, head red. The rockery is indicated only by outline; the shepherd
and hunters in solid yellow, with faces red and details red, their figures outlined in green.
The animals are gayer: yellow with stripes of green, black with yellow stripes, red with

detail   *detail*

yellow tail, and the huddling rabbits are yellow with red ears, except one that is black, outlined in red, with staring white eyes. The drama of the hunt is emphasized by the colors.

At one end, cover is badly worn, or unfinished, wide border almost completely missing. Cover lined with cotton.

For references and bibliography, see Acc. no. 1953–123–1.

Exhibited: Royal Ontario Museum, "Origins of Chintz," April 7–May 24, 1970.

Illustrated: *Origins of Chintz* by John Irwin and Katharine B. Brett, figure 17, page 27.

Published: "Some Coromandel Chintzes," by Ebeltje Jonxis, *Bulletin of the Needle and Bobbin Club*, volume 53, numbers 1 and 2, pages 37–57, 1970.

4 PALAMPORE, cotton, painted and dyed; Coromandel coast, Madras, second half eighteenth century
L. 12 feet   w. 8 feet 9 inches
Purchased   *Acc. no. 1968-78-2*

Colors: two reds, two greens, blue, yellow, violet, brown. Cotton very fine, now a biscuit color, and glazed.

Design: A large center field, and border 20 inches wide. Field is decorated with all-over pattern of small detached flower sprays, large corner clusters of naturalistic flowers (carnations, iris, and marigolds among them) and a center ornament consisting of similar flower sprays, jutting from a small round medallion, the arrangement forming a handsome star-shaped decoration. The center medallion, 7 inches wide, frames the emblem of the Pious Pelican. Above her is seen a winged serpent. The prevailing color in the large flower groups is red, the small all-over patterns are of all colors mentioned.

detail

The wide border, contained between two narrow guard borders with pattern of delicate flowering vine, exhibits a design of five types of palm trees—the Palmyra palm, banana, coconut, betel, and date palms—growing in a row, and forming a repeat pattern. On the ground appear a mongoose, a lamb, and shaggy gray dog wearing a collar. Several of the trees variously inhabited: the coconut palm is being ascended by the "toddy" man, equipped with ladder, sack, and other tools, to gather the fluid which will make the "toddy" wine. A parakeet with red body and green tail clings to the trunk of a banana palm; a cobra is coiled round the trunk of the date palm, reaching toward birds which flutter about their nest; brown squirrels are busy on the trunk of the betel palm. The palm trunks are in red, or brown, or blue with red and blue foliage.

Note: We are indebted to Dr. Robert Read for identification of the palms and to Secretary S. Dillon Ripley for the birds and animals.

5   PALAMPORE, cotton, painted and dyed; West India, Gujarat, early eighteenth century
L. 8 feet   w. 7 feet 2 inches
Purchased, Au Panier Fleuri Fund   *Acc. no. 1956-51-1*

Colors: two reds, blue, green, yellow.

Design: a large central field with powdered pink ground, corner and center ornaments, and finished with a wide border decorated with flowers on white ground. The field of pink ground has, in the center, a circular medallion reserved on white ground, framing a symmetrical arrangement of a pineapple (?), branching stems bearing heavy flowers, and a pair of confronted birds. A pointed corner ornament, with curved edge, outlined in green, frames a symmetrical floral pattern, with confronted birds at base. At center end and center side, an ornament of tightly curving leaves, now blue, forms a medallion framing large flower in red. At intervals over dotted red ground are designs in balanced arrangement of flower clusters, birds, and flying creatures: in these, some yellow appears as in a parrot with yellow head, green wings and tail, and red body. Most of the foliage is bluish as the yellow has faded.

Wide border, white ground, decorated with actively drawn flowering vine having pointed leaves, almost bird-like in movement, and various long-tailed birds perched amid branches and flowers.

Painting: the technique is fine, and sure; the design shows no European influence, suggests Persian pattern, with the undercurrent of Chinese influence. The powdered or speckled ground is made by tossing mordant for red over that area.

detail

6   PALAMPORE, painted and dyed cotton; Coromandel coast, from a Dutch
center; second half eighteenth century

L. 8 feet 5 inches   W. 11 feet 9½ inches

Purchased   *Acc. no. 1968-78-1*

Colors: two reds, blue, a delicate gray-violet (faded purple?); yellow only apparent in one or two small places is elsewhere completely faded so that the foliage leaves are blue.

Design: a double design, repeating at top and at bottom in opposite directions, consists of a tree rising from a mound, branching symmetrically into limbs which rise and curve inward to meet toward center, from which point depends a large exotic flower. Various flowers bloom on the tree; birds on mound, butterflies in open areas. Center of the palampore, a circular medallion in decorated red frame, surrounded by a wreath—possibly to suggest laurel—and surmounted by a crown. The medallion frames two naked winged figures bearing flowers, and is supported below and above by another pair of naked winged figures holding aloft a tray of flowers and bearing flower sprays. The figures are flesh color, outlined in red. Knots of ribbon adorn the medallion.

In the corners of the main design are jars in strong red, with acanthus leaf decoration, from which spring flower clusters rather naturalistically drawn; carnations and roses are recognizable.

A border, 14 inches wide surrounds the palampore, decorated with very large, elaborately painted flower clusters, on short stems, each rising from a small mound. The same flowers are used in these groups, alternating, with some changes in foliage. Narrow guard borders separate the wide border from main design and edge the palampore.

Character of painting: The flowers are rich, heavy, and elaborately painted with stripes of different color, or dotted, over a ground color. The leaves are the familiar heavy, curved type seen in crewel embroidery; many have red centers, red stems. The outlines of much of the pattern, of iron mordant, are faded and rotted.

Condition: frail, worn.

7　FRAGMENT, cotton, painted and dyed; Coromandel coast, probably made for the Dutch market, first half eighteenth century
L. 46 inches　w. 18½ inches
Purchased　　　　　　　　　　　　　　　　　　　　　*Acc. no. 1968-78-5*

Fragment is seamed in center; pieced at bottom.

Colors: two shades of strong red, two of purple; green, blue, yellow, outlines black.

Design: The portion of the pattern we see is composed of two large palmettes, of imbricated design in red, and purple, with green central stem. They slant right and left from the center and appear to emerge from a cluster of leaves, of blue, yellow, and red, outlined in black. Right and left, projecting from the palmettes are clusters of narrow, sharply pointed leaves in green, red, and yellow. Below these are leaves in blue with heavy black outlines. The whole pattern is outlined in a fine, dark wavy line, drawn about ⅛ inch from the leaves.

Pieces added at the bottom show parts of another large design. A glaze remains on the material.

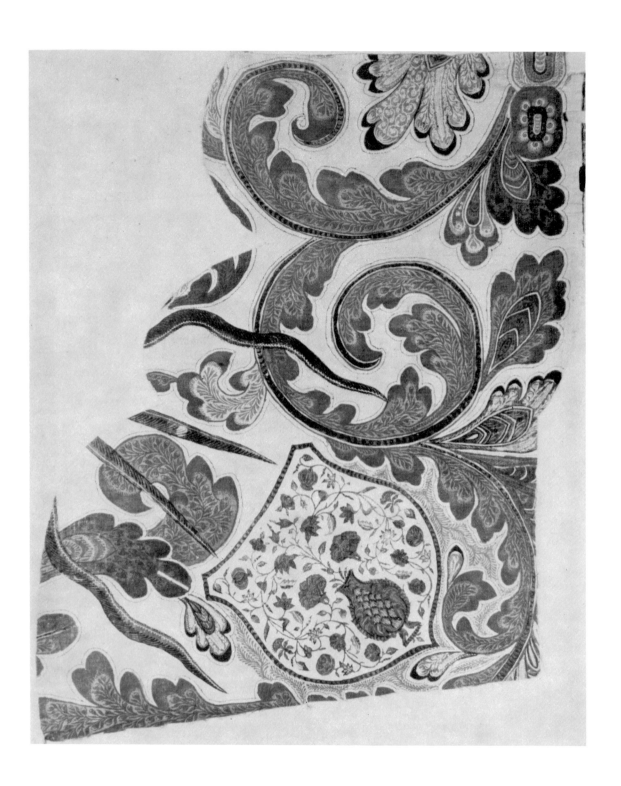

8   FRAGMENT, unevenly shaped, cotton, painted and dyed; Coromandel coast, made for the Dutch market, first half eighteenth century

L. 2 feet 8½ inches   w. 2 feet 4¾ inches

Purchased   *Acc. no. 1968-78-6*

Colors: two reds, blue, two purples; some yellow appears in narrow lines outlining inner decoration in red leaves, but has disappeared from larger leaves, which are now blue.

Design: Incomplete. A shield shape, with blue outlines, frames a jar from which spring a flowering vine of naturalistic small flowers. Large, actively curving leaves (possibly fern?) in red, purple, some in blue, several with strong blue stems and exhibiting fine inner decoration. Narrow, spear-shaped leaves project and cross heavy foliage; a very fine curving line in brownish purple outlines the whole design, drawn about ¼ inch from the pattern.

Reference: compare Baker, *Calico Painting . . . in the East Indies . . .* plate XVII. The Rijksmuseum, Amsterdam, possesses a complete palampore in this design and an embroidered palampore in the same design, worked in two shades of blue. The Victoria and Albert Museum also owns a chintz palampore in this design (IS 41–1950). See *Origins of Chintz* by John Irwin and Katharine B. Brett, catalogue number 88, plate 85.

9 LARGE FRAGMENT, uneven shape; cotton, painted and dyed; Coromandel coast, first quarter eighteenth century
L. 3 feet 7¼ inches   w. 3 feet 7 inches
Given by John Carter Brown   *Acc. no. 1961-19-1*

Colors: red, blue, green, yellow, light brown, violet.

Design: a large scale, symmetrical arrangement of curving bands, painted in great detail, forming arcs which frame stylized plant and flower forms; heavy broad leaves cross the arcs, projecting into adjoining design areas. The pattern suggests and is undoubtedly derived from a European silk brocaded in the so-called "lace pattern" style of the early eighteenth century.* The curved bands and many parts of the leaves, and other design areas, are painted with fillings: dots, minute squares, and triangles in precise arrangements. In the arcs, areas of small scale, hexagonal-sided net suggest the ground of lace, with heavy points at one side and the inner sides of the arcs edged with fine points.

The colors are predominantly red, soft green for leaves and centers of stems; yellow, violet in shades, and some blue occur; some overpainting of blue lines on red leaves. Much of the painting of the small fillings is in brown. Repeat 25 inches long, by 23½ inches wide.

Panel much pieced and faded.

Exhibited: Royal Ontario Museum, "Origins of Chintz," April 7–May 24, 1970.

Illustrated: *Origins of Chintz*, John Irwin and Katharine B. Brett, page 114, figure 56.

*See Peter Thornton, *Baroque and Rococo Silks,* pages 109–115, plates 26A, 34A, 55A, 57A.

detail

10 PALAMPORE, cotton, painted and dyed; Coromandel coast, from a Dutch center, first half eighteenth century

L. 11 feet 9¾ inches   w. 8 feet 8¾ inches;   border 18¾ inches.

Purchased, Au Panier Fleuri Fund

Acc. no. 1953-21-2

Colors: two reds, pink, two blues, small areas of red-violet, a few vestiges of pale yellow. As yellow has practically disappeared there is no green.

Design: Irregularly repeating pattern of two floral elements. One consists of bulging vase shape from which springs a cluster of leaves and above that various graceful flowers. And from the base of the vase, decorated in red with pale blue leaves, emerges a forked shape, possibly to suggest a root system. The colors in this element are shades of red, blue, and touches of faded yellow. The second spray of flowers consists of foliage, and two groups of fleshy leaves in reds, separated by circlets of blue (formerly green) with red dots; more delicate flower sprays spring from this group.

Border, 18¾ inches wide, is set between two guard bands of small festoons of flowers, and finished with a deep blue edge. The pattern in the border is the same as that in the main design except that the direction follows the line of the border.

A space of 72 inches has been cut off one side to the depth of 20 inches—slightly more than the width of the border, leaving corner pieces, and on the other side the outer guard border has been cut away.

Colors are, except yellow, fresh and agreeable. Much shading, veining, fine patterns reserved in the blue areas.

The character of the design is unreal and compares to the "bizarre" patterns in silks, a name introduced by Vilhelm Slomann in *Bizarre Designs in Silks*, translated from the Danish by Eve M. Wendt, 1953. (Though one may not agree with the author's theory we must admit he has coined a useful term.) The bizarre character of the painted cotton is probably due to the painter's misunderstanding of a pattern supplied him.

For a further study of the bizarre silks, see Peter Thornton, *Baroque and Rococo Silks*.

For the festoon border of the cotton, see Henry-René d'Allemagne, *La Toile Imprimée et les Indiennes de Traite*.

The palampore is lined with modern white cotton.

Published: Jean E. Mailey, "Indian Textiles in the Museum's Collection," *Chronicle of the Cooper Union Museum*, volume 2, number 5, June 1953.

detail

11   COVER, or part of a hanging; cotton, painted and dyed; Golconda, Coromandel coast, early eighteenth century
L. 9 feet 5¾ inches   W. 4 feet 6 inches
Purchased, Au Panier Fleuri Fund   *Acc. no. 1959-146-1*

Colors: two reds, green, two blues, yellow, purple, gray-violet, light brown; on deep red ground.

The cover has a wide border, sewn by hand to the body of the piece, along left side and across bottom. The design is related in color, but is completely different from the design of the cover.

Design of main section: a repeat pattern, of three scenic elements, in a variety of rich colors and shades on a deep red ground. Under a gnarled tree with flattened leaves appear two cranes, one perched on a pointed rock, one standing in a dark shallow pool. A second

detail

scene shows a bird (heron ?) crouched on a nest, in or near a pool or swamp of triangular shape, in which delicate plants and smaller herons are visible. From the air a bird swoops toward this pool. A third scenic element is not easily decipherable; a barred triangular shape from which rise dotted oblongs, a long stem, ending in a lotus fruit, but looking more like a lantern on a pole. These different scenes are divided by blocks of little birds, and flower clusters, of red and blue. The tree has a light brown trunk, leaves of green veined in yellow, and of blue with veining in white reserve; the big cranes are in shades of the same light brown, with red heads and beautiful feather markings. The swamp or pool in the next scene is a pale gray violet with little birds and plants reserved in white. The crouching bird on nest is in light brown and red; below this appears another pool, in blue. Although the design is crowded, the several elements have considerable delicacy. Japanese influence is apparent, particularly in the drawing of the trees and the birds.

The border consists of a series of handsome large flower heads, one a lotus, and big notched green leaves, on a red ground; reds, purples, blue notes, and much reserved decoration in the flowers, enrich the design.

See cover of this catalogue.

Exhibited: "Origins of Chintz" Royal Ontario Museum, April 7–May 24, 1970.

Illustrated: page 103, figure 53, in *Origins of Chintz* by John Irwin and Katharine B. Brett.

Compare palampore, collection of the Royal Ontario Museum (963.13), illustrated in above publication, plate 86, catalogue number 90. Several of the same design elements are used, on a white ground, but differently disposed to fit the shape of the palampore. The catalogue description suggests, "it is clearly related to other chintzes based on Japanese painted and stencilled cottons from Okinawa."

Compare also, in the same collection (959.112), catalogue number 102, illustrated plate 96, in above publication, a man's morning gown of cotton, with red ground and design of pine trees, showing similar Japanese influence.

detail

12 QUILT, center of painted cotton; lined with dark green glazed linen, and with wide border of green silk. Center made of two breadths of cotton, one of 15 inches, one of 19½ inches, seamed; Coromandel coast, first half eighteenth century

Purchased in memory of Julia Hutchins Wolcott   *Acc. no. 1968-79-1*

Colors: two reds, blue, green, yellow, brown, plum color; black for stems and details.

Design: A repeat pattern, balanced, symmetrical; flower sprays and flowering vines, in formal enframements for paired confronted birds as peacocks with spread wings, squirrels, butterflies, flowers, fruit, and other birds. Red and light red predominate, with green for foliage, birds' wings, reddish-brown for other birds, and touches of plum color. Much inner detail in flowers. Birds about 3½ inches, flower spray 5½ inches.

The additions of the lining, border of silk, and quilting were made in Europe.

detail

13   PETTICOAT, cotton, painted and dyed; Coromandel coast, for a Dutch market, first half eighteenth century

L. 38 inches   w. across bottom 63 inches

Purchased, Au Panier Fleuri Fund   *Acc. no. 1957-188-1*

Colors: two reds, two blues, yellow, green, red violet, gray-violet, and black.

Design: At bottom of skirt a broad border of a series of arches developed from curved bands of flowers, rising to sharply pointed ovals of blossoms. Between points of arches appear jars of flowers. The arched spaces frame, alternately, clusters of various blooms, or crossed, sharply pointed curved flower bands.

The bottom of the skirt is finished by a border 5¾ inches wide of small arches, reversed top and bottom, in blues, with red flowers on dotted red ground; crossed by a red band with floral decoration in blue or reserved in white.

The painting of the flowery arches is elaborate and a feathery effect is produced by a background, under flowers, of minute foliage forms in red, or dotted grounds of red; or, at sides of arches or flower clusters, feathery detail in black.

In the open space above the border are detached sprays of natural size flowers in various colors, tulips and roses among them.

All painting is in strong colors, and while the arches exhibit fine technique, the flower clusters above the border are rather heavy.

Material glazed; skirt lined with stiff white linen; one seam. At top set into waistband of green twill tape.

Reference: This type of arch decoration is commented on by Ebeltje Jonxis in "Some Coromandel Chintzes," *Bulletin of the Needle and Bobbin Club*, volume 53, numbers 1 and 2, pages 37–57, New York, 1970.

For illustrations of similar designs on petticoats, see *Origins of Chintz* by John Irwin and Katharine B. Brett plates 98 A and 98 B, catalogue numbers 105 and 106, Victoria and Albert Museum, IS 13–1950 and IS 48–1950, respectively.

14 PAIR OF CURTAINS, formerly part of a set of bed hangings; cotton, painted and dyed, made of several kinds of chintz; central panel, Coromandel coast; bands, western India. Second quarter eighteenth century

L. 9 feet 2 inches   w. 2 feet 11 inches

Purchased in memory of Julia Hutchins Wolcott   *Acc. no. 1968-79-3 a and b*

Colors: two reds, two greens, two blues, yellow, violet, orange (red over yellow).

Design: The curtains are composed of several different kinds of chintz, in an elaborate arrangement of patchwork, sewn to a lining of white linen. A series of bands, of different chintzes, forms a total design of baroque character, borders, corner motifs, and, when the curtains are edge to edge, a large central medallion. The bands are edged with cord, couched in red, which covers the seams.

The chintzes are all characterized by designs of small flower sprays, painted with great elaboration of detail, and in many contrasts of color. There is much overpainting as green on violet, one blue on another shade of the same, red over yellow to give orange, stripes of different colors in one blossom, all with great skill and delicacy of line. The leaves are sharply pointed and brightly colored. While many of the small flowers look deceptively like European blossoms, none are recognizable except a carnation. In one or two sections there are parts of a curious pattern showing narrow curving bands, one with jagged edges in red, one imbricated, red, blue, and yellow. While the ground of these chintzes is white, several of the appliqué bands are blue grounds.

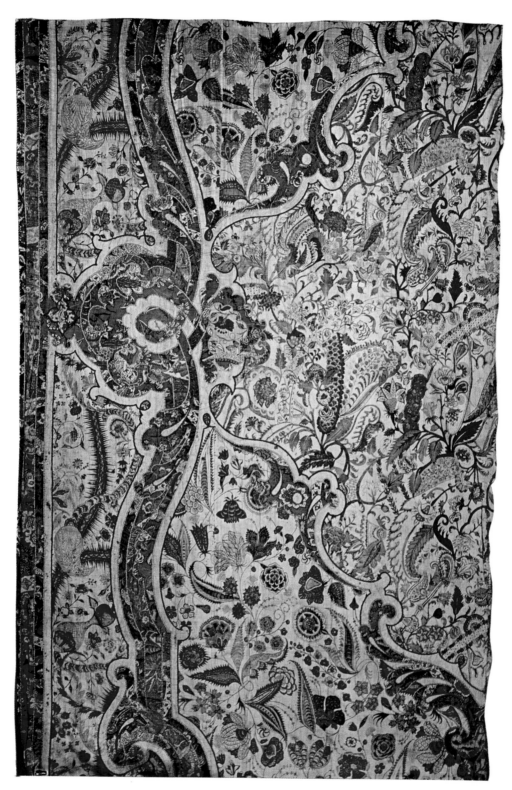

detail

15 FRAGMENT, cotton, painted and dyed; Coromandel coast, from a Dutch center, first half eighteenth century

L. 39 inches   w. 24 inches

Purchased, Pauline Riggs Noyes Fund   *Acc. no. 1952-113-1*

Colors: two reds, two blues, yellow, green, and small areas of violet.

Design: a repeat pattern of sprays of various small or natural-size flowers and foliage, which meet, and cross, forming a graceful all-over design. Strong reds in blossoms, with yellow, blue, and green in foliage. Much fine interior design within leaves or flowers, as minute white flower sprays within a red leaf or tiny red flowers on a dark green leaf. The richness and yet delicacy of this pattern recalls that favorite seventeenth-century phrase, "curious and lively colors."

The repeat is 32 inches long; there are no selvages; the cotton is fine, shows a glaze and is now dark with age.

16   FRAGMENT, of uneven shape; cotton, painted and dyed; Coromandel coast, first half eighteenth century
L. 41¼ inches   w. 19¼ inches
Purchased   *Acc. no. 1968-78-8*

Colors: two shades of red, pink, blue, a gray-violet (faded purple), brown and red for outlines.

Design: White cotton, on which a strongly curved vine appears, from which spring various large flowers. The foliage is now blue as the yellow has disappeared. Blossoms in reds, pink: some show details of a gray-violet. Drawing is heavy, bold, emphatic; flowers seen in profile are realistically drawn; naturalistic veining in leaves. Emphasis is given the forms of flowers by a trick of leaving a very narrow white space between the edge of petals and the outlines, which are sometimes red, sometimes brown. Among the flowers the tulip and carnation are identifiable.

Fragment is pieced across center.

detail

17 FRAGMENT, part of a wide border; cotton, painted and dyed; Coromandel coast, mid-eighteenth century

L. 5 feet 7 inches   w. 1 foot 8 inches

Purchased, Au Panier Fleuri Fund   *Acc. no. 1959-205-1*

Colors: two reds, two blues, a faded brownish violet; soft rose, black.

Design: A repeat pattern, in horizontal arrangement. A series of small pavilions, in which appear women in European dress, seated on high backed chairs. In spaces between these pavilions, are, alternately, a small flowering tree with stumpy little palms, and, in wider space, a rose tree, with two men on either side, in European dress. An arched effect is produced by symmetrical arrangements of foliage and flowers, surmounting the spaces between the small pavilions. In space above appear incomplete parts of a pattern of detached flowers, with bees flying. Colors of the flowers, blue, red, and in arches a soft rose. The drawing of the European figures is naive and clumsy. One of the ladies, in red bodice and blue tinted skirt is about to feed a dog from a bowl; the other lady is in red, and holds a fan in one hand, a flower in the other. Their hair is dressed high in top knots, with what, in one or two appear to be attempts at flowers, and several show streamers at the back which may be attempts to represent cap lappets. The men wear red knee-breeches; one, seated, wears a coat with blue decoration; the other man, standing, wears a coat of a light violet-brown; and carries a sword. His right hand is stretched toward the flowering tree, his left is undiscoverable. Both men wear brimmed hats with low dark crowns; long hair hangs from under their hats, possibly wigs. The little pavilions and what appears to be a walk, or floor, are in two shades of the same light brownish violet, as is the coat of the standing man. Below this scene are parts of flower heads where the material is cut.

Published: Ebeltje Jonxis, "Some Coromandel Chintzes," *Bulletin of the Needle and Bobbin Club*, volume 53, numbers 1 and 2, pages 37–57, New York, 1970.

Reference: The Victoria and Albert Museum has a bedcover, made from a skirt, which has a border of arches of flowers framing scenes with European figures (IS 42–1950).

See *Origins of Chintz* by John Irwin and Katharine B. Brett, catalogue number 108, plate 99. Attribution, Coromandel coast, southern region, third quarter eighteenth century. Made for a Dutch market.

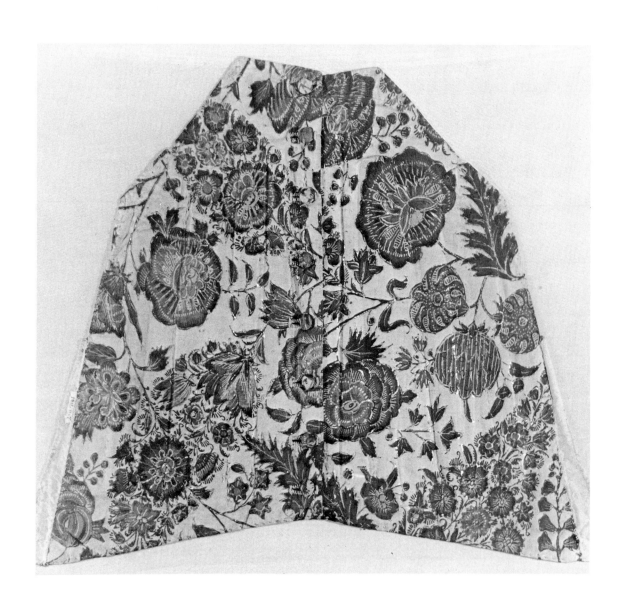

18 PART OF A BODICE, cotton, painted and dyed; probably Coromandel coast, from a Dutch center, first half eighteenth century
L. 14 inches   w. 14½ inches at top
Given by Mrs. Abram S. Hewitt   *Acc. no. 1911-11-7*

Two fronts of a woman's bodice, with eight buttons made from the chintz; buttonholes worked in white.

Colors: dark and light blue, red, green, yellow; gold leaf.

Design: Various flower heads on slender stems, largely in shades of blue with red centers; sprays of smaller flowers in red and blue; some yellow is left in two notched leaves of green. Much veining in flowers by wax resist. Outlines of larger flower heads show gold leaf and gold accents for petals and veining. Bodice front lined with white silks and boned.

Published: Jean E. Mailey, "Indian Textiles in the Museum's Collection," *Chronicle of the Cooper Union Museum*, volume 2, number 5, June 1953, pages 144–145; figure 8.

19 FRAGMENT, roughly cape shaped; cotton, painted and dyed; Coromandel coast, second half eighteenth century

L. 16 inches   w. 23½ inches

Given by J. Pierpont Morgan, ex. coll. Badia   *Acc. no. 1902-1-974*

Colors: two reds, two blues, red-violet, yellow, green; outlines black.

Design: Repeat pattern of a lattice formed of two elements, one of these elements being a cornucopia ending in a flower head of red and blue, repeated in alternating positions; clusters of blue berries and leaves attach to body of the cornucopia; the curved forms are painted reddish violet, with greenish-yellow dots in the center stripe. Remains of gold leaf outline the design and accent details of the flowers.

Piece lined with plain white silk.

Published: Jean E. Mailey, "Indian Textiles in the Museum's Collection," *Chronicle of the Cooper Union Museum*, volume 2, number 5, June 1953, pages 135–150, figure 7.

Reference: *Bulletin of the Royal Ontario Museum*, number 17, page 9, June 1953. They have in their collection a cope made for the Armenian market in the same design, dated 1787.

Origins of Chintz, by John Irwin and Katharine B. Brett. Catalogue number 186, reference to same cope. Illustrated, plate 153B.

20 PALAMPORE, cotton, painted and dyed; Coromandel coast, Pondicherry, mid to third quarter eighteenth century

L. 11 feet   w. 7 feet 9 inches

Purchased, Au Panier Fleuri Fund

Acc. no. 1952-118-1

Colors: two reds, blue, green, red-violet, yellow now much faded, red-brown outlines. Ground is now almost a biscuit color; and it is without seam.

Design: a center field and border in a repeat pattern. The field is dominated by a tall, straight, slender palm (possibly date(?)), rising from a mound, with a full crown of feathery foliage and fruit clusters. From lower on the trunk spring, at one side, small palm head, bending gracefully, and from the other side of the trunk a down-curving branch of blossoms. From the mound grows a slender flowering vine, which divides above the lower branches of the palm and winds upward, forming a frame for the tree's head, and at the top curving in, almost meeting.

Small flowering trees grow from either corner of the mound; to the left of the palm is a short, rugged tree, bamboo shoots close to the trunk of the palm, and to the right stands a handsome peacock. The trunk of the palm is marked with an eliptical pattern, and its roots are exposed.

The border, 15 inches wide, is a repeat pattern of short trees, with at center of each side, and in each corner, a small bamboo tree. The rows of little trees grow from a curving ground line, suggesting mounds. The palampore is lined with cotton.

Published: Jean E. Mailey, "Indian Textiles in the Museum's Collection," *Chronicle of the Cooper Union Museum*, volume 2, number 5, June 1953, pages 135–150, figure 4.

detail   *detail*

21   PALAMPORE, quilted, with French block printed cotton added as wide border; cotton, painted and dyed; South India, east coast, about 1750
L. 7 feet 9 inches   w. 8 feet 8½ inches
Given by Mrs. Roger Brunschwig   *Acc. no. 1969-128-1*

Colors: two reds, blue, yellow, green, brown.

Design: A field exhibiting three date palms with feathery heads, one crossing stem of the tallest, and a border of flowering vine. The palms rise from a mound; in hillocks rather naturalistic in drawing, shaded, red, green, brown, with some purple and yellow. Small bamboos rise from its corners. The trunks of the palms are purple, outlined in black; they show a scaly or imbricated surface. Vines with red stems creep up around the palm bearing small flowers in red, violet, and other colors which fill the background.

A very narrow border divides the main field from a border 10 inches wide decorated with a curving vine, like bamboo, with red and green leaves, fruits, flowers.

A wide border, 17 inches, at the sides and 7½ inches at the bottom has been added, of European, probably French, block printed cotton on a deep cream ground. The flowers are small, in reds, blues, greens, brown, in typical, small flower patterns of the block printing, second half of the eighteenth century. The quilt is lined with a rather coarse material, probably a heavy linen, block printed in large scale designs of large red flower and meander on broken black ground. The material is unbleached, and is in three breadths and a half breadth. The additions were made in Europe, France probably, and quilted, the quilting lines crossing the palampore and the added French border. The stuffing is cotton.

Reference: compare Victoria and Albert Museum, a palampore showing two date palms, crossed, attribution South India 1750–1800 (I.M. 85-1937). See *Origins of Chintz* by John Irwin and Katharine B. Brett, plate 59, catalogue number 61.

22 FRAGMENT, corner of a cover; cotton, painted and dyed, Pondicherry? last quarter eighteenth century

L. 3 feet 6 inches   w. 2 feet 8 inches

Purchased   *Acc. no. 1968-78-7*

Colors: two reds, blue, a few small areas of yellow now much faded.

Design: On a white field, in detached arrangement, freely drawn flower sprays in shades of red on delicate brown stems, with foliage now blue. A corner ornament of symmetrically curving leaf scrolls in red and blue forms a medallion, in which at its base a small section, formed of C scrolls in blue, frames confronted birds on dotted red ground. Birds' wings overpainted in small blue dabs. A narrow guard border frames the main section, below which a border, 12 inches wide, is similarly decorated with the same flower sprays and edged with the same narrow guard border; in the latter small three-leaved red flowers suggest the form of a clover leaf.

The general character of the design is very free, sketchy in style; the blue in the leaves uneven, as though pencilled in, but vestiges of yellow indicate the former presence of green. Reds in flowers shaded but no elaboration of veining employed. The whole design suggests a European embroidery pattern, or a block printed pattern of the late eighteenth century.

Piece is newly lined with plain white cotton.

23 PANEL, cotton, painted, dyed and gilded; Madras or Pondicherry; third
quarter eighteenth century
L. 4 feet 9 inches   w. 3 feet 8 inches
Purchased, Au Panier Fleuri Fund   *Acc. no. 1958-95-1*

Colors: two reds, blue, green, yellow, violet, a plum color, light gray-violet. Much gold
in outlines and painting of many areas.

Design: A lattice plan is developed in bands, composed of fine groups of little sheaves
of grain, painted in fine lines of dark blue and red, with blue tips, and in gold, crossing to
form a diamond-shaped ground. At points of meeting of the gilded bands, there are flower
clusters in various colors, and gold. Three different patterns of flowers occur at these points;
alternate clusters have dark green leaves curving down and crossing under the gilded bands.
Within the diamond shapes are small detached leaf designs. The painting shows great
delicacy and minute detail. The colors are fresh and the gold adds much to the effect.

The pattern suggests the plan of eighteenth-century French embroideries.

24   PANEL, half of a palampore, cotton, painted and dyed; last quarter eighteenth century

L. 8 feet 10 inches   w. 3 feet 11½ inches

Purchased   *Acc. no. 1968-78-3*

Colors: two reds, two blues, green, yellow, brown, dull violet.

Design: A trunk, in brilliant light red, rising from a mound, curves heavily right, then branches toward top. Various flowers occur in brilliant red, one or two in dull violet, leaves in two shades of blue with red accents; vestiges of yellow in leaves in small flower clusters. To left of curved trunk appears a half medallion formed of ribbon knots and flowers, framing a cluster of roses. The mound is of pointed hillocks in reds, blues, browns with much shading. A handsome pheasant in many colors is perched on a short plant rising from the mound, and a small flowering tree is at the right end. Birds in branches above are babblers. Finishing the right side and top, a border, 12½ inches wide, is composed of narrow festoons of ribbon and small flower clusters, and an outer festoon simulating pale rose-colored ribbon, with flower clusters at each curve, in reds, blue, pale violet. A narrow band of red, painted along the edge at right side and across top.

The piece is of very fine cotton, glazed, and now fragile; a patch of different chintz is in center of mound at bottom.

25　PALAMPORE, quilted; cotton, painted and dyed; Madras, second half eighteenth century

L. 8 feet 4½ inches　w. 6 feet 6½ inches

Given by Mrs. Benjamin Ginsburg　　　　　　　　　*Acc. no. 1969-129-2*

Colors: two reds, blue, brownish purple; yellow has disappeared so that foliage is now blue.

Design: A central field, with trees, and wide border with flowering vine. A tree, with exposed roots, rises from the point of a triangular mound; branches about half way up where limbs appear sawed off. A vine, rising from the mound crosses and recrosses the tree, bearing large flowers in reds, some 6 inches across, and foliage now blue. The flowers exhibit much interior decoration in reserved patterns.

Birds, babblers, are perched amid branches and two long-necked cranes on the mound, on either side of the tree. The mound is made of a series of diamond shapes, 2 inches across: a row of red alternates with a row of blue and purple diamonds. They bear fine inner decoration of fine sprays of flowers, reserved in white. The crane at the right of the tree has a back wing which is an applied patch, painted material in pattern similar but not the same as that of his companion.

Border, 12 inches wide between two very narrow guard borders, decorated with vine in brown bearing large heavy flowers in red, possibly lotus. Pointed leaves in chevron of red and blue, with outlines of dark brown.

26 PANEL, part of a hanging; cotton, painted and dyed; provenance unknown, possibly western India, second quarter eighteenth century

L. 9 feet 7½ inches   w. 2 feet 3½ inches

Purchased in memory of Julia Hutchins Wolcott   *Acc. no. 1968-79-2*

Colors: two reds, two blues, two violets, yellow, black and brown.

Design: A curving tree trunk, rising from a mound, with various flowers of marked European character, drawn with great naturalism: roses, the buds and stems of which show thorns; carnations, morning glories, columbine (?), dahlias, tulips. Tree trunk, mound, and outlines brown; foliage green; flowers, two shades of red, blue, reddish-brown and a violet now faded. All flowers show much detail of shading. Along right side and bottom a border in blue-green, in wavy curved outline over which flowers project. Panel cut at top; small patch of self chintz on reverse of top; bottom, small patch of plain white cotton reverse.

Exhibited: "Origins of Chintz," Royal Ontario Museum, 7 April–24 May, 1970.

Reference: A panel of the same design in collection of the Royal Ontario Museum: 934.4.25, catalogue number 60, plate 58.

Illustrated: *Origins of Chintz* by John Irwin and Katharine B. Brett, figure 38.

27 QUILT, made from a palampore, cotton, painted and dyed; western India, mid-nineteenth century

L. 8 feet 11 inches   W. 9 feet 5½ inches

Purchased   *Acc. no. 1968-78-4*

Colors: two reds, dark and light brown, pale yellow-brown; remains of light blue in a few large flowers and a few border flowers; black.

Design: From a large mound, painted in shades of red, brown, and black, rises a cluster of eight bamboos, which branch toward the sides and top. The bamboos are twined with vines bearing flowers.

From the corners of the mound grow flowering trees in the branches of which parakeets and squirrels disport themselves. The bamboo trunks are alternately red and brown. Most of the flowers are in shades of red except for a few large blossoms which are now white, with veins of black, but tree trunks at sides are brown and foliage yellowish brown with dark brown veins. In the upper branches are several large birds in black and brown, identified as babblers, and the parakeets are red, with tails in light and dark brown. In the mound, which is painted in a good deal of detail in conventionalized points and curves to suggest hillocks, are several large blossoms in red, one in browns, and groups of animals (deer?) in red.

The entire background of the chintz is painted with a minute feathery pattern of foliage, in a light yellowish brown.

A border, 17½ inches wide, in a formal design of flower garlands and ribbons, edges the entire quilt, except the lower corners, left and right, where it has been cut away to fit a bed. Originally the border was painted in one with the main design, as seen at the bottom of the quilt, but the cover has been shortened at the top, thus clipping off the tips of the bamboos, and cut into at the sides. Where these alterations have taken place the border is sewn by hand to the body of the quilt.

detail

28 DETAIL from border of a palampore, cotton, painted and dyed; Coromandel
coast, last quarter eighteenth century
L. from tip to tip 18½ inches
Given by Mrs. Florence Peto   *Acc. no. 1955-113-1*

Colors: red, blue, violet, brown, yellow visible in small spots.

Design: A swag of flowers, with leaf above, butterfly below, and guard stripe of
narrow vine at edge.

Reference: Compare, border of a palampore, Royal Ontario Museum, 934.4.12, illustrated *Origins of Chintz* by John Irwin and Katharine B. Brett, plate 31, catalogue number 33.

29   INFANT'S DRESS, cotton, painted and dyed; Coromandel coast, Madras or
      Pondicherry, second half eighteenth century
      L. 32 inches   w. at shoulder 12 inches
      Given by Mrs. Robert P. Brown   *Acc. no. 1960-81-9*

      Colors: red, blue, lavender, brown.
      The dress is an example of the thrift of an earlier day, for, though the material is
eighteenth century, the dress is made in the style of the first quarter of the nineteenth
century.
      This infant's dress is from the effects of Mrs. Pierre Van Cortlandt III, (1818–1895).

30 PALAMPORE, cotton, painted and dyed; collection, Historic Cherry Hill, Albany, New York

L. 9 feet 4¼ inches   w. 7 feet 4½ inches

The tree rising from a jagged mound, with much feathery foliage and flowers, fills the center field; a border is decorated with a curving vine bearing many flowers. The mound is of unusual interest as it is inhabited in various places by people in European dress, animals, and birds.

A palampore of the same design is in the collection of the Royal Ontario Museum, accession number 934.4.11, number 26 in the catalogue in *Origins of Chintz* by John Irwin and Katharine B. Brett, published in 1970. It is there attributed to the Coromandel Coast?, first half eighteenth century.

Cherry Hill, a house built in what is now Albany in 1768 by Philip and Maria (Sanders) Van Rensselaer. The palampore was found several years ago in the attic of the house in a trunk with other eighteenth-century textiles, and is believed to have been used by that family.

31 PALAMPORE, cotton, elaborately embroidered in brilliantly colored silk in
    chain stitch; India, Gujarat, second half eighteenth century
    Museum of Fine Arts, Boston, Massachussetts   *Acc. no. 57. 168*

The tree rises from a small compact mound, with little flower clusters in crevices; from its serpentine branches grow a variety of brilliant flowers, long heavily notched leaves, and a pineapple. The border is composed of a series of small, heavy trees, with trailing branches of flowers. The character of the embroidery is extremely interesting as it exhibits an attempt to employ, in stitches, all the various tricks of marking, inner decoration, striping, shading, and other elaborations which the painted cottons display. The result is brilliant and handsome. The design and its characteristics are another evidence of the theory that the palampores and embroidered covers such as this, or our Ashburnham curtain and palampore, must come from a common pattern source.

The Boston Museum has given us an unimpeachable line of descent through a family for this piece, too long to give in full. It is known to have been the property of Dorothy Lynde, who married Dr. Elijah Dix; she may have inherited it from her father, Joseph Lynde, 1703–1780. It was given the Museum by Mrs. Frank M. Clark, 14 January, 1957.

32 PALAMPORE, painted and dyed. India, Coromandel Coast(?) second half
eighteenth century
Collection of the Henry Francis du Pont Winterthur Museum
Gift of Miss Gertrude Brincklé

The tree, with serpentine trunk, rising from a mound shows a variety of blossoms
with elaborate inner decoration. At either corner of the mound are jars filled with flowers.
The handsome border is decorated with a luxuriant flowering vine, which springs from a
jar at either corner of the bottom.

History: According to the donor the palampore is known to have been owned in Maryland in the eighteenth century, either by a member of the Brincklé, the Boyer, or the Rumsey
families.

33 PALAMPORE, provenance unknown, probably Coromandel coast, nineteenth century
L. 8 feet 8 inches   w. 7 feet 1 inch
Essex Institute, Salem. Massachussetts   *Acc. no. 123, 328*

Colors: reds, blue, yellow, green, brown.

Design: a tree rising from a mound, behind which appears a bamboo, the stem of which shades from blue into yellow. Blossoms on large tree, red, as are those on small trees at side. Mound is brown, light brown, yellow, and red, with red flowers; animals are red, the lion is a dull yellow with red spots. Some greens remain, as in bamboo leaves, but they are rather uneven. The border, with conventional flower swags in red, green-blue, with red ribbons, is distinguished by pineapples growing stiffly from pots, which are shaded from red to rose. The birds perched on either side of the pineapple are red with green tails and wings. The edge of the palampore is finished with a wavy line, in red, green, purple, and brown, marked by tips of little projecting plants.

The pineapple was introduced into India by the Portuguese in the sixteenth century. Many of the later travelers encountered it for the first time with pleasure. There is an amusing incident which occurs early in the journal of Sir Thomas Roe, when the agravating governor of Surat attempts to placate Sir Thomas with the gift of pineapples. ". . . Soe giving me two pines, with a long speech of the dayntenes, which I bade a servant take, telling him I knew the fruict very well, I took my leave."*

History of the palampore: Brought from India by William Dean Waters (1798–1880). Given to the Essex Institute by William C. Waters, 1938.

* *The Embassy of Sir Thomas Roe to India, 1615–1619.* . . . Edited by Sir William Foster, London, Oxford University Press, 1926, page 48.

34 PALAMPORE, cotton, painted and dyed; Coromandel coast, last quarter eighteenth century
L. 108 inches   w. 88 inches

The palampore, in the collection of the Rhode Island Historical Society is now exhibited in the John Brown House, built in 1786, a historic house owned by the above society and located near its headquarters in Providence. The initials *P.L.* embroidered on the palampore, stand for Penelope Low who married Charles Lippitt in 1783; through the descendants of this family this interesting cover came to the Rhode Island Historical Society.

Colors: red, blue, blue-green, and a violet-brown for outlines.

Design: A bamboo and a second tree grow close together on a mound, both showing exposed roots. Their limbs cross and blossoms of various kinds grow from the branches, among which a rose is recognizable. On the mound, confronting each other on either side of the trees, stand two peacocks with cobras in their beaks; below appear prancing leopards (or lions?) and another bird. The border, of delicate intertwined garlands, emerging from vases at either of the lower corners, shows marked European influence.

Reference: A palampore, in the collection of the Royal Ontario Museum (934.4.3) illustrated at plate 38, catalogue number 36 in *Origins of Chintz* by John Irwin and Katharine B. Brett, shows the same border. At plate 40 in the same work, catalogue number 41, is shown a palampore from the collection of the Victoria and Albert Museum (IS38–1950) which has the same arrangement of trees and branches. Peacocks holding cobras in their beaks appear on a palampore illustrated at plate 52 in the same work.

The palampore in the John Brown House has been altered to fit a bed, and, according to information from a member of the staff of the Rhode Island Historical Society, a seal of the British East India Company was found on a piece removed for the alteration.

Bibliography

Allan, John and H. H. Dodwell, editors. *Cambridge Shorter History of India*. Cambridge, Cambridge University Press, 1934.

Allemagne, Henry-René d'. *La Toile imprimeé et les indiennes de traite*. 2 volumes. Paris, Gründ, 1942.

Allen, Beverley Sprague. *Tides in English Taste (1619–1800), A Background for the Study of Literature*. 2 volumes. Cambridge, Harvard University Press, 1937.

Archer William G. *Indian Painting in Bundi and Kotah*. London, Her Majesty's Stationery Office, 1959.

Baker, George Percival. *Calico Painting and Printing in the East Indies in the XVIIth and XVIIIth Centuries*. London, E. Arnold, 1921.

Barbosa, Duarte. *The Book of Barbosa; An Account of the Countries Bordering on the Indian Ocean and Their Inhabitants, Written by Duarte Barbosa, and Completed About the Year 1518 A.D.* Translated from the Portuguese by M. Longworth Dames. 2 volumes. London, Hakluyt Society, 1918–1921.

Beekman Mercantile Papers, 1746–1749. 3 volumes. New York Historical Society, New York, 1956.

Beer, Alice. "Why Textiles?" In *Chronicle of the Cooper Union Museum*, volume 2, number 7, June 1955.

Bernier, François. *Travels in the Mogul Empire A.D. 1656–1668*. Translated by Archibald Constable, 1891. 2nd edition revised by Vincent A. Smith. London, Oxford University Press, 1914.

Birchwood, George, and William Foster, editors. See *The First Letter Book of the East India Company, 1600–1619*.

Blacker, Irwin R., editor. *Hakluyt's Voyages Selected from the Third and Last Voyages*. (London, 1600) New York, Viking Press, 1965.

Bowrey, Thomas. *Geographical Account of the Countries Round the Bay of Bengal, 1669–1679*. London, Hakluyt Society, 1905.

Boxer, C. R. *The Dutch Seaborne Empire, 1600–1800*. London, Hutchinson & Co., 1965.

Breck, Joseph. "Four Seventeenth-Century Pintadoes." In *Metropolitan Museum Studies*. New York, Metropolitan Museum of Art, 1929, pages 3–15.

Brett, Katharine B. "Chintz, an Influence of the East on the West." In *Antiques*, volume LXIV, number 6. New York, December 1953, pages 480–483.

———. "An English Source of Indian Chintz Design." In *Journal of Indian Textile History*, number I. Ahmedabad, Calico Museum of Textiles, 1955, pages 40–53.

———. "A French Source of Indian Chintz Design." In *Journal of Indian Textile History*, number II. Ahmedabad, Calico Museum of Textiles, 1956, pages 43–52.

———. "The Flowering Tree in Indian Chintz." In *Journal of Indian Textile History*, number III. Ahmedabad, Calico Museum of Textiles, 1957, pages 45–57.

———. "Variants of the Flowering Tree in Indian Chintz." In *Antiques*, volume LXXVII, number 3. New York, March 1960, pages 280–283.

———. "The Japanese Style in Indian Chintz Design." In *Journal of Indian Textile History*, number V. Ahmedabad, Calico Museum of Textiles, 1960, pages 42–50.

Bruce, John. *Annals of the Honorable East India Company.* . . . London, Black, Parry and Kingsbury, 1810.

Cambridge Shorter History of India. See Allan, John and H. H. Dodwell, editors.

Chandra, Moti. "Costumes and Textiles in the Sultanate Period." In *Journal of Indian Textile History*, number VI. Ahmedabad, Calico Museum of Textiles, 1961, pages 5–61.

Chardin, John. *The Travels of Sir John Chardin into Persia and the East Indies; The First Volume Containing the Author's Voyage from Paris to Ispahan to Which Is Added the Coronation of the Present King of Persia, Solyman the Third*. London, Moses Pitte, 1686.

Charpentier, François. *A Treatise Touching the East-Indies Trade; Or, A Discourse (Turned*

Out of French Into English) Concerning the Establishment of a French Company for the Commerce of the East-Indies to Which Are Annexed the Articles, and Conditions, Whereupon the Said Company for the Commerce of the East-Indies Is Established. Edinburgh, Anderson, 1695.

Clouzot, Henri. *Histoire de la manufacture de Jouy et de la toile imprimée en France.* Paris, Les Éditions G. Van Oest, 1928.

Culin, Stewart. "The Story of the Painted Curtain." In *Good Furniture Magazine*, volume XI. Grand Rapids, Michigan, September 1918, pages 133–147.

Cust, Lionel. "Notes on the Collections Formed by Thomas Howard, Earl of Arundel and Surrey. Part II: A Memorial of All The Rooms at Tart Hall and An Inventory of the . . . Goods There Belonging to the . . . Countess of Arundell . . . 1641." In *Burlington Magazine*, volume 20. London, October 1911–March 1912, pages 97–100, 233–236, 341–343.

Danvers, F. C., and W. Foster, editors. See *Letters Received by the East India Company . . .*

Dawn of British Trade to the East Indies as Recorded in the Court Minutes of the East India Company 1599–1603 . . . Original manuscript by Henry Stevens. Introduction by George Birchwood. London, Henry Stevens, 1886.

Defoe, Daniel. *The Trade to India Critically and Calmly Consider'd; and Proved to Be Destructive to the General Trade of Great Britain as well as to the Woollen and Silk Manufacturers in Particular.* London, Boreham, 1720.

Delhi. Indian Art Exhibition. *Indian Art at Delhi, 1903*, official catalogue by Sir George Watt. Calcutta, Superintendent of Government Printing, 1903.

Digby, George Wingfield. "Lady Julia Calverley: Embroideress." In *Connoisseur*, volume 145. London, March–June, 1960.

Dos Passos, John. *The Portugal Story; Three Centuries of Exploration and Discovery.* Garden City, N.Y., Doubleday & Co., Inc., 1969.

Downer, Marion. *The Story of Design.* New York, Lothrop Lee and Shepard, 1963.

East Indian trade, Selected Works, 17th Century: A collection of five rare works republished from the originals in the Goldsmith's Library of Economic Literature, the University of London, by kind permission of the librarian. 2nd impression. Westmead, Farnborough, Hants, England, Gregg International Publishers Ltd., 1969.

The English Factories in India, 1618–1641. Edited by William Foster. Oxford, Clarendon Press, 1906–1912.

Evelyn, John. *Diary and Correspondence.* New York, Scribner's, 1906.

Fiennes, Celia. *The Journals of Celia Fiennes.* Edited by C. Morris. London, 1947.

The First Letter Book of the East India Company 1600–1619. Edited by George Birchwood and William Foster. London, 1892.

Federici, Cesare de'. "Voyage." Translation in *Hakluyt's Voyages*, volume 3. London, Hakluyt Society, 1927.

Fitch, Ralph. "The Long, Dangerous and Memorable Voyage of R. F." In *Early Travels in India*, edited by William Foster. London, 1921.

Foster, William, editor. See *The English Factories in India, 1618–1641.*

Fryer, John. "A New Account of East India and Persia." London, Hakluyt Society, 1909–1912, 2nd series.

Glamann, Kristof. *Dutch-Asiatic Trade, 1620–1740.* Copenhagen, Danish Science Press, 1958.

Grousset, René. *The Civilizations of the East, the Near and Middle East.* Translated by Catherine Alison Phillips. New York, Alfred Knopf, 1931.

Hadaway, William Snelling. *Cotton Painting and Printing in the Madras Presidency.* Madras 1917.

Hannay, David. *The Great Chartered Companies.* London, Williams and Norgate, 1926.

Havard, Henry. *Dictionnaire de l'ameublement et de la decoration depuis le XIIIᵉ siècle jusqu'à nos jours.* volume 3. Paris, Maison Quantin, no date.

Havart, Daniel. *Op-en ondergang van Coromandel.* 3 volumes, Amsterdam, 1693.

Heyd, Wilhelm von. *Histoire du commerce du Levant au moyen-age. Société de l'Orient Latin, par Furcy Raynaud.* Amsterdam, A. Hakkert, 2 volumes, 1967.

Hudson, Geoffrey Francis. *Europe and China; a*

Survey of Their Relations from the Earliest Times to 1800. London, Arnold, 1931.

Irwin, John. "The Commercial Embroidery of Gujerat in the Seventeenth Century." In *Journal of the Indian Society of Oriental Art*, volume 17. Calcutta, 1949 (issued 1952).

————. "Indo-Portuguese Embroideries of Bengal." In *Art and Letters: Journal of Royal India and Pakistan Society*, volume 26, number 2. London, 1952.

————. *Shawls; a Study in Indo-European Influences.* London, Victoria and Albert Museum Monograph, 1955.

————. "Origins of the 'Oriental Style' in English Decorative Art." In *Burlington Magazine*, volume 96. London, April 1955, pages 106–114.

————. "Indian Textile Trade in the 17th Century." In *Journal of Indian Textile History*, numbers I–IV. Ahmedabad, Calico Museum of Textiles, 1955–1959.

————. "Origins of 'Oriental' Chintz Design." In *Antiques*, volume LXXV, number 1. New York, January 1959, pages 84–86.

————. "Golconda Cotton Paintings of the Early Seventeenth Century." In *Lalit Kalā* (Journal of the Indian Academy of Art), number 5. New Delhi, April 1959, pages 8–48.

————. "Insignia of the English East India Company." In *Journal of Indian Textile History*, number IV. Ahmedabad. Calico Museum of Textiles, 1959, pages 78–79.

————. "Some Dated Textiles in the Victoria and Albert Museum." In *Journal of Indian Textile History*, number V. Ahmedabad, Calico Museum of Textiles, 1960, pages 60–71.

————, and Katharine B. Brett. *Origins of Chintz.* London, Her Majesty's Stationery Office, 1970.

————, and Paul R. Schwartz. *Studies in Indo-European Textile History.* Ahmedabad, Calico Museum of Textiles, 1967.

Jonxis, Ebeltje. "Some Coromandel Chintzes." *Bulletin of the Needle and Bobbin Club*, volume 53, numbers 1 and 2, New York, 1970.

King, Donald. "Textiles." In *Connoisseur's Complete Period Guides*, New York, Bonanza, 1968.

Krishna, Vijay. "Flowers in Indian Textile Designs." In *Journal of Indian Textile History*, number III. Ahmadabad, Calico Museum of Textiles, 1967, pages 1–20.

Letters Received by the East India Company from Their Servants in the East. Volumes I–VI, edited by F. C. Danvers and W. Foster. London, Low, Marston, London, 1896–1902.

Linschoten, John Huyghen van. *The Voyage of John Huyghen van Linschoten to the East Indies; from an Old English Translation of 1598.* 2 volumes, edited by A. Burnett and P. A. Tiele. London, Hakluyt Society, volumes LXX, LXXI, 1885.

Lockyer, Charles. *An Account of the Trade in India; Containing Rules for Good Government—Trade, Price Courants, and Tables; with Descriptions of Ft. St. George, Acheen, Malacca . . . the Cape of Good Hope, and St. Helena . . . to Which is Added, an Account of the Management of the Dutch in Their Affairs in India.* London, the author, 1711.

Mailey, Jean E. "Indian Textiles in the Museum's Collection." In *Chronicle of the Cooper Union Museum*, volume 2, number 5. New York, The Cooper Union Museum, June 1953.

Master, Streynsham. *Diaries, 1675–80.* Edited by Richard Carnac Temple, 2 volumes. London, John Murray for the Government of India, 1911.

Montagu, Mary W. *Complete Letters of Lady Mary Wortley Montagu.* Volume 1, 1708–1720. Edited by Robert Halsband, London, Oxford University Press, 1966.

Morris, Frances. "An Indian Hanging." In *Bulletin of the Metropolitan Museum of Art*, volume 20. New York, Metropolitan Museum of Art, 1925, pages 143–152.

Morrison, Samuel Eliot. *The Maritime History of Massachusetts 1783–1860.* New York, Houghton Mifflin Co., 1921.

Munday, Peter. *The Travels of Peter Mundy, 1634–1638.* Edited by Richard Carnac Temple. London, Hakluyt Society, 1914–1919, numbers 35, 45, 46.

Naqvi, Hameeda Khatoon. "Dyeing of Cotton Goods in the Mughal Hindustan, 1556–1803." In *Journal of Indian Textile History*, number VII. Ahmedabad, Calico Museum of Textiles, 1967, pages 45–46.

Nevinson, John Lea. *Catalogue of English Domestic Embroidery of the Sixteenth and Seventeenth Cen-*

turies. London, Victoria and Albert Museum, 1938.

————. *The Embroidery Patterns of Thomas Trevelyan*. The Walpole Society, volume XLI, 1966–1968.

Nowell, Charles E., editor. *Magellan's Voyage Around the World; Three Contemporary Accounts by Antonio Pigafetta, Maxmilian of Transylvania, Gaspar Correa*. Evanston, Illinois, Northwestern University Press, 1962.

O'Neill, Charles. *A Dictionary of Dyeing and Calico Printing*. Philadelphia, Henry Carey Baird, 1869.

Parkinson, C. N. *Trade in the Eastern Seas, 1793–1813*. Cambridge, University Press, 1937.

Parks, George Bruner. *Richard Hakluyt and the English Voyages*. Edited and introduced by James A. Williamson, 2nd edition, New York, Ungar, 1961.

Peabody, Robert E. *Merchant Venturers of Old Salem; a History of the Commercial Voyages of a New England Family to the Indies and Elsewhere in the XVIII Century*. Cambridge, Houghton, Mifflin & Co., 1912.

Pelsaert, François. *Remonstrantie*. Translated by W. H. Moreland and P. Geyl from the Dutch under the title, *Jahangir's India*. Cambridge, Heffer, 1925.

Pepys, Samuel. *Diary and Correspondence of Samuel Pepys*, volume II. New York, Bigelow, Brown, no date.

Periplus of the Erythraean Sea; Travel and Trade in the Indian Ocean by a Merchant of the First Century, The. Edited and Translated by Wilfred H. Schoff. New York, Longmans, Green & Co., 1912.

Pfister, R. *Les toiles imprimées de Fostat et l'Hindoustan*. Paris, Les Éditions d'art et d'histoire, 1938.

Phillips, James Duncan. *Salem and the Indies*. Boston, Houghton Mifflin, 1947.

Pillement, Jean. *Fleurs, Oiseaux et Fantasies*. Paris, H. Ernst, 1924.

Pires, Tomé. *The Suma Oriental of Tomé Pires; an Account of the East from the Red Sea to Japan, Written in Malacca and India 1512–1515; and the Book of Francisco Rodrigues, Rutter of a Voyage in the Red Sea, . . .* 2 volumes, edited and translated by Armando Cortesão. London, Hakluyt Society, 1944.

Purchas, Samuel. *Purchas His Pilgrimes*. 4 volumes, London, 1625.

Purefoy, Elizabeth and Henry. *The Purefoy Letters 1735–1753*. Edited by E. Eland. 2 volumes. London, Sidgwick & Jackson, 1931.

Raaschou, Dorte. "Un document Danois sur la fabrication des toiles peintes à Tranquebar, aux Indes, à la fin du XVIIIe siècle." *Bulletin de la Société Industrielle de Mulhouse*, number 729/IV. Mulhouse, 1967.

Raychaudhuri, Tapan. *Jan Company in Coromandel, 1605–1690; a Study in the Inter-Relations of European Commerce and Traditional Economies*. 'sGravenhage, Martinus Nuhoff, 1962.

Robinson, Basil W. *Persian Miniature Painting from the Collections in the British Isles*. London, Her Majesty's Stationery Office, 1967.

Robinson, Basil W. *Persian Paintings*. London, Her Majesty's Stationery Office, 1965.

Roe, Thomas. *The Embassy of Sir Thomas Roe to India 1615–1619; as Narrated in his Journals and Correspondence*. Edited by William Foster, new and revised edition. London, Oxford University Press, 1926.

Rosengarten, Frederic, Jr. *The Book of Spices*. Wynnewood, Pennsylvania, The Livingston Publishing Co., 1969.

Rowse, A. L. *The England of Elizabeth; the Structure of Society*. London, Macmillan & Co., Ltd., 1951.

Rye, William B. *England as Seen by Foreigners in the Days of Elizabeth and James the First . . .* London, John Russell Smith, 1865.

Schoff, William A., editor and translator. See *Periplus of the Erythraean Sea . . . .*

Schwartz, Paul R. "L'application du bleu d'indigo." In *Bulletin de la Société Industrielle de Mulhouse*, number 2. Mulhouse, 1953, pages 63–79.

————. "French Documents on Indian Cotton Painting, Part I; The Beaulieu Manuscript, c. 1734. In *Journal of Indian Textile History*, number II. Ahmedabad, Calico Museum of Textiles, 1956, pages 5–23.

————. "French Documents on Indian Cotton Painting, Part II: New light on Old Material."

In *Journal of Indian Textile History*, number III. Ahmedabad, Calico Museum of Textiles, 1957, pages 15–44.

————. "The Roxburgh Account of Indian Cotton Painting 1795." In *Journal of Indian Textile History*, number IV. Ahmedabad, Calico Museum of Textiles, 1959, pages 47–56.

————. "Les toiles peintes Indiennes." In *Bulletin de la Société Industrielle de Mulhouse*, number 4. Mulhouse, 1962, pages 3–23.

————. "La fabrique d'Indiennes du Duc de Bourbon, 1692–1740." In *Bulletin de la Société Industrielle de Mulhouse*, number 722/I. Mulhouse, 1966.

————. "L'impression sur coton à Ahmedabad (Inde) en 1678 d'après un manuscrit inedit de la Bibliothéque Nationale à Paris." In *Bulletin de la Société Industrielle de Mulhouse*, number 726/I. Mulhouse, 1967.

Seherr-Thoss, Sonia P. *Design and Color in Islamic Architecture: Afghanistan, Iran, Turkey*. Washington, Smithsonian Institution Press, 1968.

Slomann, Vilhelm. *Bizarre Designs in Silks, Trade and Traditions*. Translated by Eve M. Wendt. Copenhagen, E. Munksgaard, 1953.

Smith, Vincent A. *The Oxford History of India from the Earliest Times to the End of 1911*. 3rd edition, edited by Percival Spear. Oxford, Clarendon Press, 1958.

Spear, Percival. *The Nabobs; a Study of the Social Life of the English in 18th Century India*. London, Oxford University Press, 1963.

Stevens, Henry. See *Dawn of British Trade . . .*

Stow, John. *Annals; or a General Chronicle of England . . . 1631*. Edited by Edmund Howes. London, R. Meighen, 1631.

Tavernier, Jean Baptiste. *Voyages en Perse; et description de ce royaume 1632–1667*. Paris, Pascal Pia, Aux éditions du Carrefour, 1930.

————. *Les six voyages de J. B. T. au Perse et aux Indes*. 2 volumes, Paris, 1676. Translated by V. Ball, London, 1899.

————. *Travels in India*. Translated by V. Ball, London, 1925.

Thevenot, Jean de. *Relation d'un voyage fait au Levant par M. Jean de Thevenot; . . . .* Paris, Thomas Iolly, 1665.

————. *Indian Travels of Thevenot and Carreri. . . .* Edited by Surendranath Sen. New Delhi, National Archives of India, 1949.

Thornton, Peter. *Baroque and Rococo Silks*. London, Faber and Faber, 1965.

Turner, Ralph L. *A Comparative Dictionary of the Indo-Aryan Languages*. London, Oxford University Press, 1964.

Valle, Pietro della. *The Travels of Pietro della Valle in India*. Translated 1664 by G. Havers, edited by Edward Grey, 2 volumes. London, Hakluyt Society, 1892.

Varthema, Ludovico di. *The Travels of Ludovico di Varthema in Egypt, Syria, Arabia Deserta and Arabia Felix, Persia, India and Ethiopia, 1503–1508*. Translated from the original Italian edition of 1510 by John Winter Jones, edited by George Percy Badger. London, Hakluyt Society, 1863.

Watson, John Forbes. *The Textile Manufacture and the Costumes of the People of India*. London, G. E. Eyre and W. Spottiswoode, 1886.

Watts, Sir George. See Delhi.

Weigart, Roger-Armand. *Chefs-d'oeuvre textiles du XVIIIᵉ siècle*. Greenwich, Connecticut, New York Graphic Society, 1964.

Yule, Henry and A. C. Burnell. *Hobson-Jobson, a Glossary of Anglo-Indian Words and Phrases*. Edited by William Crooke. London, J. Murray 1903.

Glossary

Banyan: **1.** A Hindu trader, and especially of the province of Guzerat, . . . but the term is often applied to persons of Hindu religion generally. In Calcutta specifically applied to native brokers attached to houses of business, or to persons in the employment of a private gentleman doing analogous duty—now *sircar*. **2.** An undershirt, originally of muslin resembling body garment of Hindu. Our predecessors in India used to adopt native costume in hours of leisure.

—Hobson-Jobson

Bombast: **1.** To stuff, pad, or fill out with cotton-wool.

Cf. Bombace,-ase (as of bombace cotton, cotton wadding: -late L. bombace-m acc. of bombax cotton, a corruption and transferred use of L. bombyx silk, a Gr. . . . silkworm, silk.) **2.** The down of the cotton-plant; raw cotton 1553 Eden Treat. New Ind. (arb.) 13. This cotton, is otherwyse called Bombage or sylke of the trees. . . .　　　　*—Hobson-Jobson*

Cadou: The cadou or myrobolan contains tannin, like the gall-nut. It acts as a dyestuff, or a mordant, or both together.

—Journal of Indian Textile History, III, page 25, note 2, 1957

Chay: choy . . . chaya, also 6. saia, 9 choya, chey, chay-root, shaya-rood. (ad. Tamil saya, in other Indian vernaculars shaya, chaya. The root of the Indian plant "Oldenlandia umbellata" (N.O. Cinconaceae) used to give a deep red dye to Indian cottons.

1598 tr. Caesar Frederike (c. 1566) in Hakluyt (Y) died with a roote which they called saia.　　　　*—Hobson-Jobson*

Chintz: A printed or spotted cotton cloth. Portuguese chita. Makr. chit. H. chint. The word

in this last form occurs (c. 1590) in the Ain-i-Akbari 1 (195). It comes apparently from the Sanskrit chitroc, 'variegated, speckled.' The best chintzes were bought on the Madras coast, at Masulipatam and Madras. The French form of the word is chite. . . .

1676 "chites or Painted Calicuts, which they call Calmendars, that is done with a pencil, are made in the kingdom of Golconda."

1666 "Le principal trafic des Hollandais à Ahmedabad, est de chites, que sont de toiles peinte." Thevenot V. 35.　　*—Hobson-Jobson*

5036—Chitta—"spotted cloth" (Cf. chitt, chat). Kamaoni, chit, 'calico,' Nepali, chit, Assamese, sit, Bengali, chit, Oriya, chita, Hindi, chit, Kashmiri, chith . . . Sindhi, chita, Panjabi, chit, Gujarati, chit f. 'chintz.'

—Ralph L. Turner, *A Comparative Dictionary of the Indo-Ayran Languages*

Corge, coorge: A score.　　*—Hobson-Jobson*

Coromandel Coast: A name formerly applied officially and later in a historical sense to the eastern seaboard of India approximately from Cape Calimere northward to the mouths of the Krishna River. The name Coromandel is said to be derived from Cholamandal, the "mandal" or region of the Chola Dynasty.

—Encyclopaedia Britannica

Covid: A measure varying locally. Corruption of the Port. covado, a cubit or ell.

1672 Measures at Suratt are the Lesser and Greater Coved, the former of 27 inches, the latter 36 inches. Fryer 206.　　*—Hobson-Jobson*

Lineal measurement used in India, its length varied at different times and places from 3 to 14 inches.　　　　*—Oxford Dictionary*

Ducat: A gold coin of varying value, formerly in use in most European countries; that current in Holland, Russia, Austria, and Sweden being equivalent to about 9s. 4d. Also applied to a silver coin of Italy, value about 3s. 6d.

—Oxford Dictionary

Ell: 45-inch measure. *—Hobson-Jobson*

Fardel: Package or bundle.

Factor: F. facteur, L. factor. One who works, or transacts business, for another, an agent. Formerly, an employee of the East India Company ranking above a writer and below a merchant.

—Webster's New International Dictionary

Factory: An establishment or trading station where factors, or commercial agents reside and transact business for their employers.

—Webster's New International Dictionary

Factor system: a system carried on by European Companies, an immemorial custom, handed down from the time of the Phoenicians.

—List of Factory Records of the Late East India Company

Ferret: (Usually believed to be ad. It. fioretti floss-silk (rendered 'ferret silk' by Florio: see quot. 1598), pl. of fioretto, dim. of fiore flower. 1. attrib. Ferret-silk-floss silk Obs.

—Hobson-Jobson

Kersey: many spelling variations. (Possibly named from the village of Kersey in Suffolk; though evidence actually connecting the original manufacture of the cloth with that place has not been found.) **1.** A kind of coarse narrow cloth, woven from long wool and usually ribbed. **2.** with a and pl. a. a piece of Kersey of a definite size obs. b. A make or variety of Kersey (chiefly in pl.)

In the 16–17th c. kerseys are commonly contrasted with cloths or broad cloths; the size of the latter was fixed by the statute of 1465 as 24 yds. long by 2 wide, while a kersey was only 18 yds. long and a yard and a nail in width. In 1557 reduced to between 16 and 17 yds. 1618–3 kersies equalled to one cloth, etc.

—Oxford Dictionary

Malabathrum: Aromatic leaf mentioned by ancient writers; ointment prepared from this (derivation of word: from Arabic: powder of the cave.) *—Oxford Dictionary*

Myrobalan: The astringent plum-like fruit of species of Terminalia (N.O. Combretaceae), eg. T. Bellerica . . . T. Chebula. . . . . , T. Citrina: formerly used medicinally but now chiefly used in dyeing, tanning, and ink-making.

—Hobson-Jobson

Orpiment: Gold pigment. A bright yellow mineral substance, the trisulphide of arsenic, also called yellow arsenic, found native in soft masses resembling gold in colour, also manufactured by the combination of sulphur and arsenious oxide used as a pigment under the name of king's gold. *—Oxford Dictionary*

Pagoda: pagod: Coin, usually gold in 1818, Rupee made standard and pagod = 3½ rupees. "Indian and Heathenish money with a picture of Divel upon them." Linschoten.

—Hobson-Jobson

Palampore: probably derived from hybrid Hindu-Persian word meaning bedcover.

Picul: (Malay-Javanese pikul a man's load (Yule); in Sp. pico.)
A measure of weight used in China and the East generally, equal to 100 catties, i.e., about 133⅓ lbs. avoirdupois.

Piece: A length (varying according to the material) in which cloth or other textile is measured. A piece of muslin is 10 yds; of calico, 28 yds. etc. (from Simmons Dictionary of Trade, 1858.) *—Oxford Dictionary*

Plunkett: plunkett. A kind of gray cloth. Wool fabric of varying texture of a gray or light blue color. Also adjective: grayish blue.
—*Oxford Dictionary*

Realgar: Native of factitious disulphide of Arsenic also called red Arsenic and red orpiment used in pigment and in pyrotechnics.

Stammet: Some woolen cloth (from stamel), a coarse woolen cloth.

Stammel also used as adjective: the shade of red in which the cloth was commonly dyed.
—*Oxford Dictionary*

Toddy.   A corruption of Hind. Tāri, the fermented sap of the tar or palmyra (Sansk. tāl) and also of other palms, such as the date, the coco-palm and the Caryota urena; palm-wine. Toddy is generally the substance used in India to leaven bread.   —*Hobson-Jobson*

CREDITS

The bill dated 1701 from the Woburn Abbey Collection is published by the kind permission of His Grace, the Duke of Bedford.

The Cooper-Hewitt Museum is grateful to the Public Records Office, London, for furnishing a photostatic copy of the page from Tax Records, 1749-1750. Exports London to New England.

The Cooper-Hewitt Museum acknowledges with gratitude permission to publish a map from the Battista Agnese manuscript, written and illuminated on vellum at Venice, circa 1540, from the Spenser Collection, The New York Public Library, Astor, Lenox and Tilden Foundations; and a map from the Rare Book Division, The New York Public Library, Astor, Lenox and Tilden Foundations, which is by A. Ortelius in *Theatre* . . . , Antwerp, 1571.

For permission to publish objects in their collections, the Cooper-Hewitt Museum thanks
The Essex Institute, Salem, Massachusetts
The Boston Museum of Fine Arts
The Rhode Island Historical Society, Providence
Historic Cherry Hill, Albany, New York
The Henry Francis du Pont Winterthur Museum, Winterthur, Delaware.

Photography by George Cowdery.

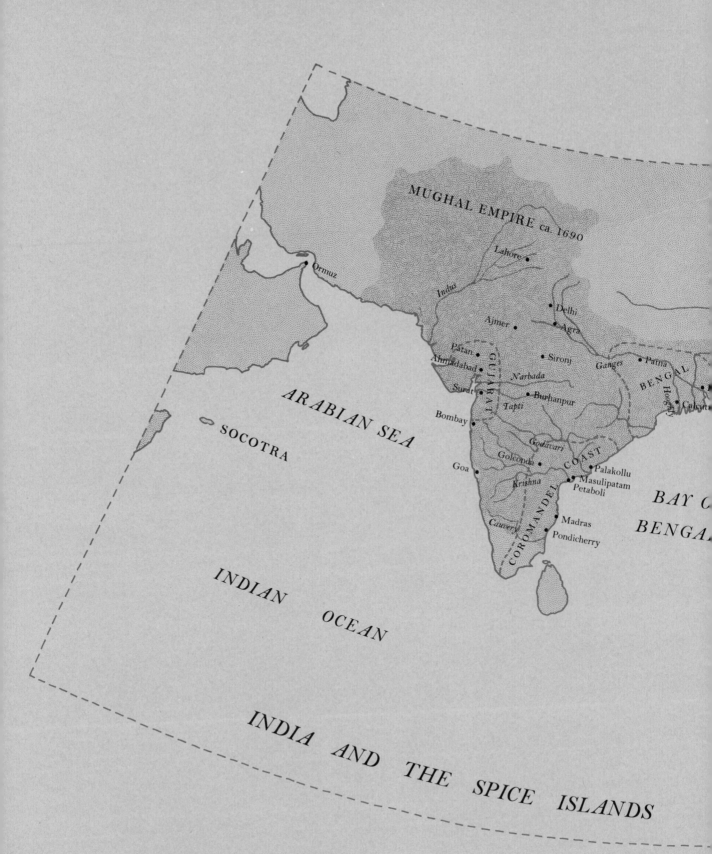

MUGHAL EMPIRE ca. 1690

Lahore

Ormuz

Delhi

Ajmer

Agra

Indus

Patan

Sironj

Ganges

Patna

BENGAL

Ahmadabad

GUJARAT

Narbada

Surat

Tapti

Burhanpur

Hooghly

Calcutta

ARABIAN SEA

Bombay

SOCOTRA

Godavari

COROMANDEL COAST

Goa

Golconda

Palakollu

Krishna

Masulipatam

Petaboli

BAY OF

BENGAL

Cauvery

Madras

Pondicherry

INDIAN OCEAN

INDIA AND THE SPICE ISLANDS